Surfing the Net Science

Inquiry-based worksheets for free
Internet videos, articles, and games.

Written by
Jennifer Katherine Brooks

Graphic Design by
Chip Dombrowski

Edited by
Ashley Fleming

© 2014
THE CRITICAL THINKING CO.™
www.CriticalThinking.com
Phone: 800-458-4849 • Fax: 541-756-1758
1991 Sherman Ave., Suite 200 • North Bend • OR 97459
ISBN 978-1-60144-663-3

Table of Contents

Overview

Computers are in every classroom and almost every home, yet many schools and parents only use preselected programs for instruction. Consequently, many students do not know how to research information using the largest information source in the world—the Internet. The *Surfing the Net: Science* activities are designed to teach students how to use the Internet to research Grades 3-6 science concepts based on standards found in most states. Students who complete this book will learn Grades 3-6 science, but more importantly how to gather information from the Internet.

How to Use This Book

Surfing the Net: Science is organized around science standards found in most states. Each topic offers a variety of research-based activities to use as supplements to teacher instruction or as student-guided instruction for curriculum unit integration. The worksheets are perfect for activating/ previewing lessons, direct instruction lessons, or culminating activities for each unit. Activities include writing assignments that incorporate creative, expository, and narrative writing standards.

Each topic covers critical thinking inquiries in five different capacities:
- **Defining:** Students use key word searches to gather general information about the topic from the Internet using text, videos, charts, or images. Students answer questions about the topic.
- **Describing:** Students use key word searches to gather specific information about the topic from the Internet using text, videos, charts, or images.
- **Analyzing and Synthesizing:** Students use the information gathered from defining and describing the topic to fill in a graphic organizer. Students may use the graphic organizer to write a paragraph.
- **Expanding Knowledge:** Students collect additional information from the Internet about something specific from the topic. Students may write paragraphs about this additional information.
- **Investigating:** Students form their own question and then find the answer through research on the Internet or an experiment.

The book may be used in a variety of ways to differentiate for the range of ages, grades, and achievement levels in your classroom. For example, younger students (Grades 3 and 4) may complete the activities as a culminating project while older students (Grades 5 and 6) may complete the activities as an introduction or activating lesson to the topic. All ages and ability levels may use the activities as review lessons.

 Some questions are designated challenge questions. Challenge questions may require additional support for younger or struggling students.

Teachers may implement the activities as whole class instruction, individual learners at a computer, center work, or group assignments. Introductions to each science section include additional websites recommended for whole group instruction. Teachers may also springboard off the key word sections for further research within a topic and use writing activities within each lesson to meet ELA standards.

To make surfing easier for students, the links for each activity are available at www.criticalthinking.com/stns so that students can click on the links rather than type them.

Activity Layout

Each activity begins with a key word search section. Since the introduction of the Internet in the 1990s, information is just a click away, but students (and teachers) can be overwhelmed by the search results. Teaching simplified key word searches is imperative. Before beginning *Surfing the Net: Science* activities, teachers are strongly advised to use the lesson on search engines and key word searches. This video lesson is available at www.criticalthinking.com/search-web.

The remaining questions in the activity direct students to specific URLs for gathering information from videos, interactive games, or virtual activities. Icons along with each URL designate what kind of an activity is involved.

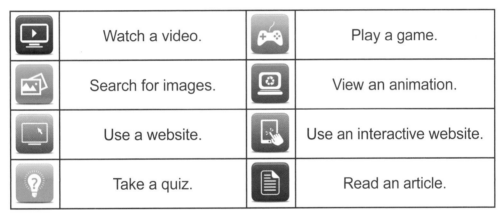

	Watch a video.		Play a game.
	Search for images.		View an animation.
	Use a website.		Use an interactive website.
	Take a quiz.		Read an article.

I spent over a thousand hours carefully selecting fun, high-interest, engaging yet educational websites for this book. I chose to include only trusted sites that are age-appropriate with research-based information to save teachers and parents much time and energy while making learning fun for the students.

In researching videos for this book, I chose not to include YouTube links. While YouTube contains excellent science videos, many are posted on the site by a secondary source and are, therefore, unreliable. Also, YouTube contains videos of every sort — many not appropriate for children. I encourage educators to search and preview videos on YouTube for each science topic and decide if any are right for your students.

Section 1

Animals

Animals are living things that cannot produce their own food, but can move around freely during all, or part, of their lives to search for their food. These are the two main attributes that separate animals from plants, which are also living things on Earth.

The animal kingdom is broken into two major groups: invertebrates (animals without backbones) and vertebrates (animals with backbones).

This section on animals presents critical thinking questions for students to search the Internet for answers.

Websites for whole class instruction:
http://animals.nationalgeographic.com/animals/

http://animal.discovery.com

http://video.nationalgeographic.com/video/kids/animals-pets-kids/

Amphibians

 Use the **key words** in each question to find the answers on the Internet.

1. Amphibians are ectothermic. How do habitats affect ectothermic animals?

   _____

   _____

   _____

2. Define metamorphosis.

   _____

   _____

3. List the most distinguishing characteristics of the three main groups of amphibians.

Group 1	Group 2	Group 3
salamanders, newts, and mudpuppies	caecilians	frogs and toads

   _____   _____   _____

   _____   _____   _____

   _____

4. What is the largest amphibian? How long is it? How much does it weigh?

   _____

   _____

5. Why is a poison dart frog dangerous to touch?

   _____

   _____

6. Animal adaptations occur when an animal changes its appearance or body functions to better fit in with its environment. Create a new amphibian that combines the unique physical adaptations of the painted chubby frog and the axolotl salamander. Use the smaller circles to record your findings. Use the larger circle to draw and label your new amphibian.

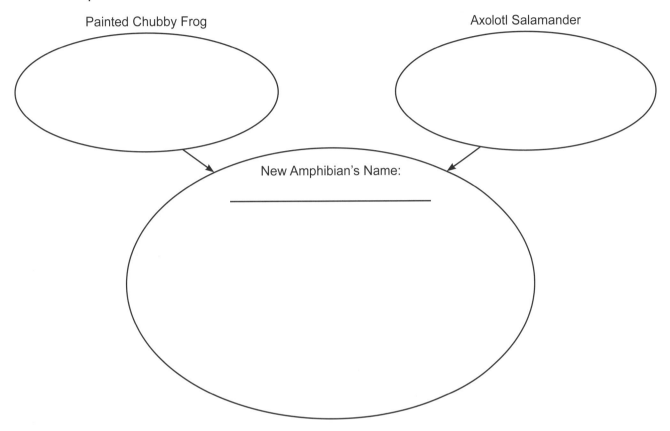

Painted Chubby Frog

Axolotl Salamander

New Amphibian's Name:
_____

7. Explain how your new amphibian uses its special adaptations.

_____

_____

_____

_____

_____

Search for pictures of the life cycle of a frog (click on **Images** after your key word search).

8. On a separate piece of paper, draw and label the life cycle of a frog.

Go to http://animals.nationalgeographic.com/animals/amphibians/ to watch *National Geographic*'s "Freak of Nature-Water Holding Frog" **video**.

9. How do the survival techniques of the water-holding frog differ from a human's in a desert environment? Use the Venn diagram to record your findings.

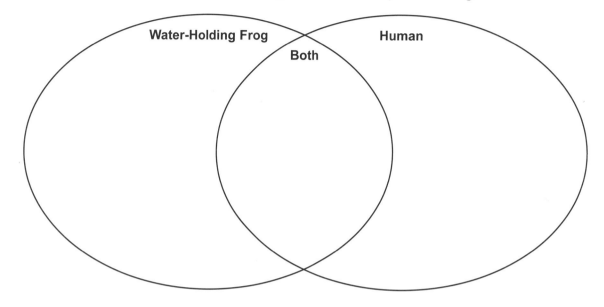

10. Explain how the survival techniques compare.

_____

_____

_____

_____

_____

Go to http://www.mydoctorgames.com/dissect-a-frog/game/ to play *My Doctor Games*' "Virtual Frog Dissection" **game** to discover the internal anatomy of a frog.

11. Why do humans dissect animals? What do we learn from seeing the inside of a frog?

_____

_____

_____

_____

Animal Cells

 Use the **key words** in each question to find the answers on the Internet.

1. Which part of the cell controls all of its functions?

   _____

2. How is a cell membrane similar to a door?

   _____

3. Which part of a cell converts food into energy?

   _____

4. Where are proteins synthesized in a eukaryote cell?

   _____

5. What is the result of mitosis?

   _____

   _____

 Search for pictures of an animal cell (click on **Images** after your key word search).

6. On a separate piece of paper, draw and label the parts of an animal cell using the words in the choice box.

mitochondrion	lysosome	nucleolus	rough ER	nucleus
cell membrane	ribosome	cytoplasm	microtubules	centrioles
pinocytotic vesicle	smooth ER	Golgi apparatus		Golgi vesicles

For questions 7-10, go to http://www.cellsalive.com/mitosis.htm to view the *CELLS alive!* "Animal Cell Mitosis" **animation**.

7. Describe the events of each of the seven phases of mitosis.

Phase Name of Mitosis	Summary of Events Occurring
1.	
2.	
3.	
4.	
5.	
6.	
7.	

8. **CHALLENGE** On a separate piece of paper, write a creative explanation about cell mitosis from the point of view of the cell. Describe how it would feel to go through each phase.

Click on the "How Big?" **animation** link on the left side of webpage. Magnify the pin to observe the actual sizes of each animal or animal cell in relation to each other.

9. Sort the examples by sizes that are smaller than a red blood cell.

smallest   biggest

					red blood cells

 Click on the interactive "Cell Cams" link on left side of the webpage. View the "Bacteria Cam" to see the bacteria growth sequence.

10. How long does it take the streptococcus pneumoniae bacteria cells to double in number?

_____

11. **CHALLENGE** Research streptococcus pneumoniae bacteria on the Internet. Fill in the hypothesis statement below about the symptoms caused by this bacteria and the speed at which it reproduces.

If a person contracts streptococcus pneumoniae, he/she will have

_____ _____, _____ _____, and

_____ _____, which will advance at a _____

(slow/rapid) rate.

Birds

 Use the **key words** in each question to find the answers on the Internet.

1. What is the scientific word for the study of birds?

   _____

2. How much heavier is the biggest ostrich than the biggest emu?

   _____

3. Why was the Audubon Society started? What year was it founded?

   _____

   _____

4. Birds are important to Earth, but they can also be nuisances. What are the benefits and disadvantages of birds in an ecosystem?

Pros of Birds	Cons of Birds

5. Based on your research, do the benefits of birds outweigh the disadvantages in an ecosystem? Explain why or why not.

   _____

   _____

   _____

   _____

6. 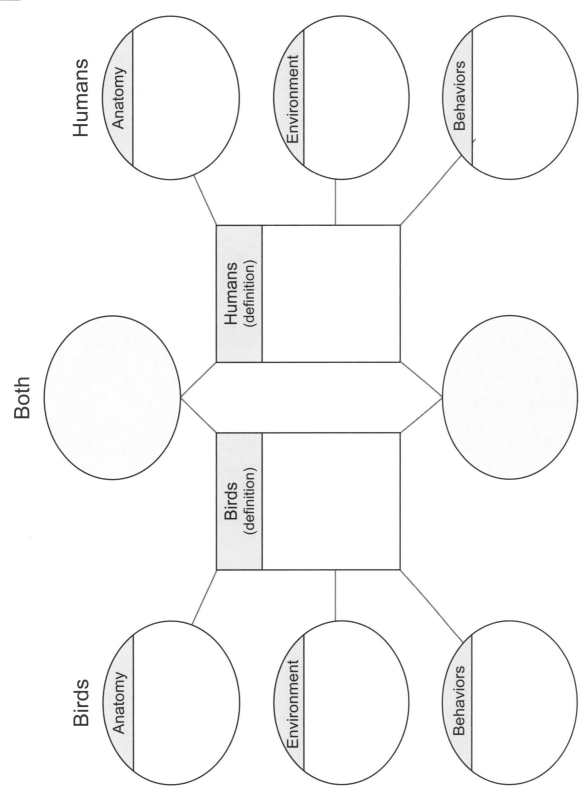 Compare and contrast birds and humans.

7. Complete the table about these unusual bird migrations.

Bird Species	Length of Migration (One Way)	Beginning and Ending Locations of Migration
North American Blue Grouse		
Rufous Hummingbird		
Arctic Tern		

Go to www.allaboutbirds.org/labs/applications/MMB/ACIntro.aspx?campaignid=4 to help *The Cornell Lab of Ornithology*'s computer, "Merlin," learn how to identify birds. Answer the questions on the website about the bird shown so you and Merlin can become bird ID wizards!

8. What species did you help the computer identify? _____

Listen to your bird before you leave the page so you can identify it even when you can't see it! Draw a picture of your bird.

9. How does answering the questions enable the computer to identify the bird species?

_____

_____

Search on the Internet for the *Audubon Society*'s Mission Migration **game** to help birds migrate.

10. Write a story about your adventures as a migrating bird. Use the chart to help you gather details about your journey to include in your story.

Type of Bird	Hazards	Sources of Energy	Health Risks
	• • •	• • •	• • •

Places Traveled	Interesting Things Seen
• • •	• • •

_____

_____

_____

_____

_____

_____

_____

_____

_____

_____

_____

_____

Fish

 Use the **key words** in each question to find the answers on the Internet.

On Earth Today

1.

Largest Mammal	Largest Fish

Weight in Tons	Weight in Tons	Difference

−   =

2. What are four main characteristics of fish?

_____   _____

_____   _____

3. How many shark attacks on humans were reported in the USA in 2012? Which state had the most?

_____

4. What is the world's deadliest fish? Why?

_____

_____

5. Why is the coelacanth considered a living fossil?

_____

_____

_____

6. Research one fish listed on the endangered species list and three causes placing the species in danger. Use the chart to record your findings.

Endangered Fish Species

Causes of Endangerment

Endangerment's Affect on the Species'

Diet	Size

Territory	Reproduction

Explain how the three causes of endangerment affect the species of fish.

_____

_____

_____

_____

_____

_____

_____

_____

For questions 7-9, go to http://library.thinkquest.org/05aug/00548/Dissection Game.html and play the "Salmon Dissection" **game**. Follow the directions to dissect a salmon.

7. List the internal organs of a salmon as you remove them from the body.

1. _____

2. _____

3. _____

4. _____

5. _____

6. _____

7. _____

8. _____

8. Draw and label the 8 internal organs you listed in the dissection activity.

9. Which organs that you labeled does the salmon have that you do not?

_____

 Go to http://dsc.discovery.com/sharks/shark-games to take the "Shark Personality Quiz."

10. Which shark matches your personality?

_____

 Sharks are at the top of the marine food chain. Search the Internet for **images** of the great white shark's food chain.

11. **CHALLENGE** On a separate piece of paper, illustrate the connection from one food source to another in the great white shark's food chain. Include at least five food sources in the shark's food chain.

Insects

 Use the **key words** in each question to find the answers on the Internet.

1. What is the scientific name of the study of insects?

   _____

2. How does a monarch butterfly transform through metamorphosis?
   Use the chart to record your findings.

Monarch Butterfly Metamorphosis

Stage 1	Stage 2	Stage 3	Stage 4
Details: • • •	Details: • • •	Details: • • •	Details: • • •

3. Describe one of the four stages.

   _____

   _____

   _____

   _____

   _____

   _____

4. What is the heaviest insect in the world? Where is it found?

   _____

   _____

5. Giant insects that attack humans in order to take over the world only exist in science fiction. In the real world, the exoskeleton prevents bugs from extremely large growth. How?

_____

_____

6. Some bugs are beneficial to humans and the environment, but some bugs are harmful. Find each insect's effect on the environment and decide if it is a good bug or a bad bug.

Insect	Effect on Environment	Helpful?	Harmful?
Japanese Beetle			
Hornworm Caterpillar			
Honeybee			

 Search for pictures of insects (click on **Images** after your key word search).

7. Draw and label an insect's three body segments.

8. Name and illustrate the 7 features shared by all insects. Then, on a separate piece of paper, create a new bug using these features.

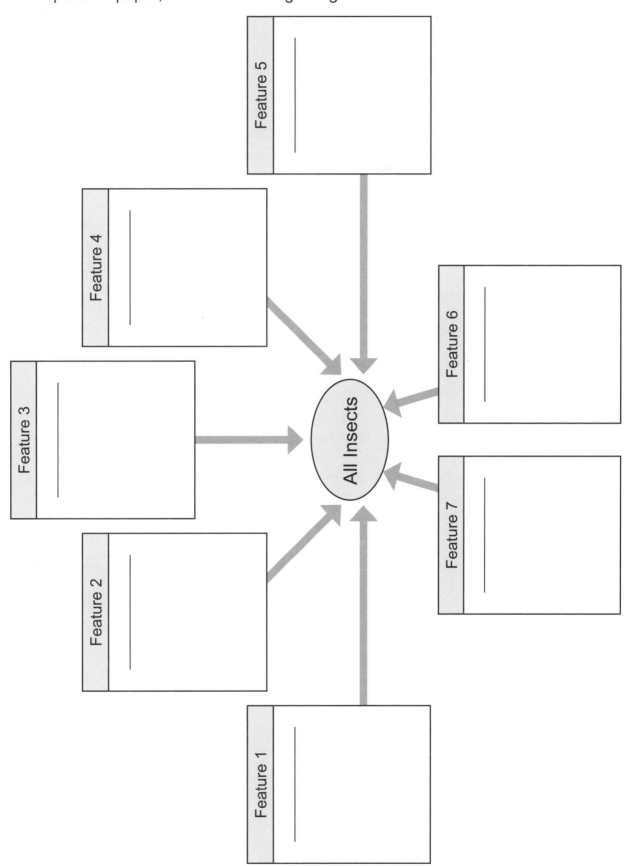

For questions 9-10, go to these insect zoo websites:
www.mnh.si.edu/education/exhibitions/insectzoo.html
www.nhm.org/site/explore-exhibits/permanent-exhibits/insect-zoo
www.keywestbutterfly.com

9. Use the chart to plan a visit to one of the zoos.

Name of Zoo	Things to See and Do
	•
	•
Address	•
Cost of Admission	

10. Create a schedule of your day by describing each hour's activities and expenses. (Don't forget to have lunch!)

Time	Activities and Expenses
10:00-11:00	
11:00-12:00	
12:00-1:00	
1:00-2:00	
2:00-3:00	
3:00-4:00	

Invertebrates

 Use the **key words** in each question to find the answers on the Internet.

1. What is the main difference between vertebrates and invertebrates?

   _____

2. Define heterotrophic.

   _____

   _____

   What living forms are NOT heterotrophic?

   _____

3. What animal is considered the first invertebrate and the exception to most of the rules defining an invertebrate?

   _____

4. What characteristics make something an echinoderm or arthropod?

   Examples of Echinoderms   **Examples of Arthropods**

   _____ _____   _____ _____

   _____ _____   _____ _____

Characteristics Shared by Echinoderms
•
•
•

Characteristics Shared by Arthropods
•
•
•

5. On a separate piece of paper, write a paragraph comparing how an echinoderm is different from an arthropod.

6. **CHALLENGE** The invertebrates in each group below belong to the same animal phylum, *except one*. Find the phylum they share and cross out the species that doesn't belong. Write the phylum name on the line.

Invertebrates	Phylum
roundworm, ~~scorpion~~, pinworm, hookworm	nematode
squid, crab, clam, mussel, oyster	
spider, shrimp, lobster, centipede, slug	
scallop, sea lily, sea urchin, holothurian	

Go to http://glencoe.mcgraw-hill.com/sites/dl/free/0078617022/167348/ 00038301.swf and view the "Invertebrates" **video**.

7. What percentage of animals on Earth are invertebrates? _____

8. Which phylum of invertebrates outnumbers every other animal on Earth?

_____

Search the Internet for **images** of invertebrates with radial and bilateral symmetry.

9. Draw an example of each below.

Invertebrate With Radial Symmetry	Invertebrate With Bilateral Symmetry

10. Look at your pictures. What is the difference between radial and bilateral symmetry?

_____

_____

_____

Mammals

 Use the **key words** in each question to find the answers on the Internet.

1. Which three features distinguish mammals from other classes of animals.

   _____

   _____

2. What are monotremes? Define and list two examples.

   _____

   _____   _____

3. What are marsupials? Define and list two examples.

   _____

   _____

   _____   _____

4. **CHALLENGE** The mammals in each group below belong to the same animal family, *except one*. Find the family they share and cross out the animal that doesn't belong. Write the family name on the line.

Animals	Family
melon-headed whale, Orca, dolphin, ~~porpoise~~	Delphinidae
sugar glider, striped possum, flying squirrel, wrist-winged glider, great-tailed triok	
lemming, lion, puma, panther, ocelot	
dingo, jackal, mongoose, wolf, Pomeranian	

5. Predict the weight (in pounds) of each animal and write it in the box. Then find the actual average weight (in pounds) of each animal. What is the difference between your guess and the actual weight?

Animal	Estimate	Actual Weight	Difference
Blue Whale			
Camel			
Raccoon			

For questions 6-8, go to http://video.nationalgeographic.com/video/kids/animals-pets-kids/mammals-kids/ to see the *National Geographic for Kids* website and watch three **videos** about different mammals.

6. List one animal from each video and name three of its unique characteristics. Use the chart to record your findings.

Mammal 1	Mammal 2	Mammal 3

Unique Characteristics

7. On a separate piece of paper, explain how one of these mammal's unique characteristics make it specially adapted to thrive in its environment.

8. Create a new mammal by combining the unique characteristics and special adaptive features of two different animals. On a separate piece of paper, draw your new mammal. Give your new mammal a species name.

Go to www.worldwildlife.org to visit the *World Wildlife Fund* **website**.

9. Research one critically endangered species of mammals. Use the chart to record your findings.

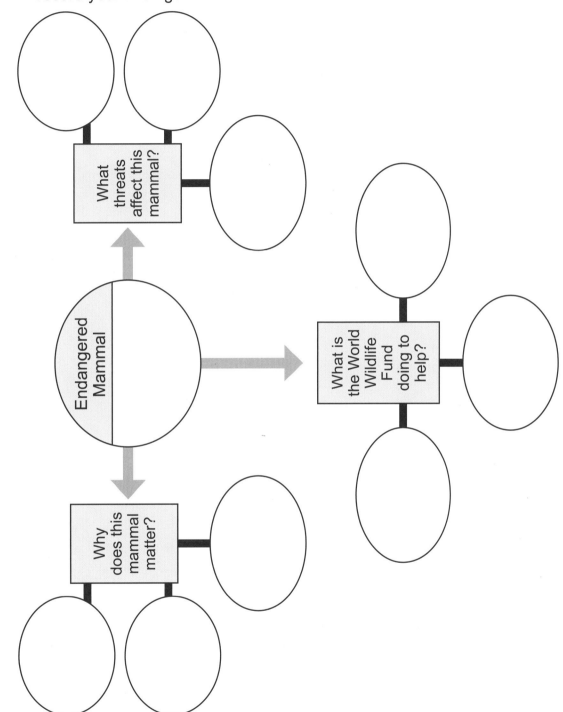

What threats affect this mammal?

Endangered Mammal

What is the World Wildlife Fund doing to help?

Why does this mammal matter?

10. On a separate piece of paper, write a letter to Congress and the President about saving the endangered mammal you researched. Explain why your mammal matters to the world. Describe the threats to your mammal and propose a way to help in saving this mammal.

Reptiles

 Use the **key words** in each question to find the answers on the Internet.

1. What are three defining characteristics of reptiles?

   _____   _____   _____

2. Why shouldn't you handle the inland taipan snake?

   _____

3. Name two reptiles that give birth to live young.

   _____   _____

4. What are the differences and similarities of alligators and crocodiles? Use the Venn diagram to record your findings.

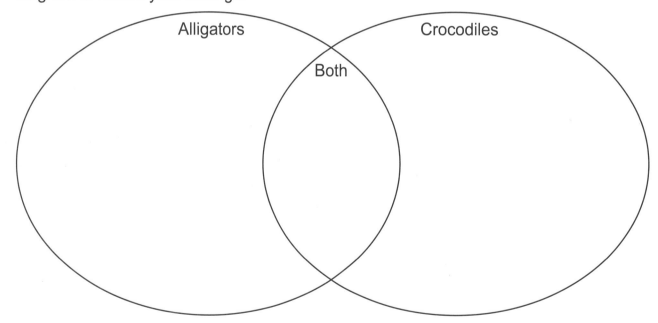

5. Why is a deadly snake considered venomous not poisonous?

   _____

   _____

   _____

For questions 6-8, go to http://www.kcc.org.nz/tuatara to the *Kiwi Conservation Club*'s "Tuatara" **website**.

6. Why are tuataras extinct on the mainland of New Zealand?

    _____

    _____

7. List three of your favorite facts from the tuatara webpage. Then explain why you think tuataras are interesting animals using complete sentences.

    _____

    _____

    _____

    _____

8. How would global warming affect the tuataras? Use the chart to record your findings.

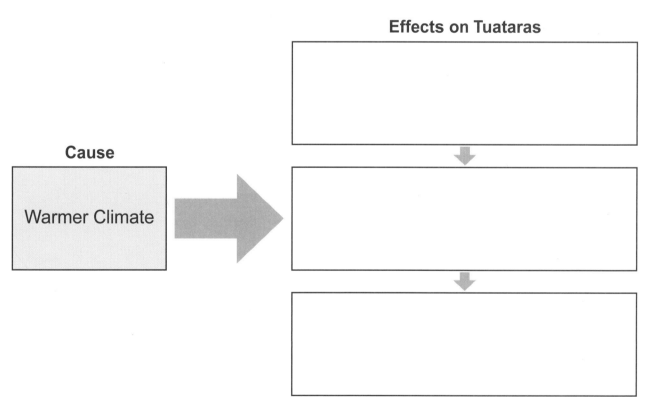

Effects on Tuataras

Cause

Warmer Climate

For questions 9-11, go to http://newswatch.nationalgeographic.com/2011/08/16/ video-from-the-field-anolemageddon/ to watch the **video** of a *National Geographic* field scientist and his reptile experiment.

9. What is the purpose of the experiment? What does the scientist hope to learn?

_____

_____

_____

10. What factors does the scientist measure during the experiment?

_____ _____ _____ _____

11. How will these factors inform him about the anoles species' competition?

_____

_____

_____

12. On a separate piece of paper, use the scientific method to plan your own experiment with reptiles.

Step	Procedure
1 Choose your topic.	What reptile would you observe? Choose any reptile in the world. Find information about your reptile on the Internet.
2 Identify a problem.	What problem does the reptile have? Consider factors such as population, habitat, predators, etc.
3 Research the problem.	Is the reptile endangered? If so, why? Is the reptile losing habitat? If so, why? Have the reptile's predators increased or decreased? If so, why?
4 Develop a hypothesis.	Make an educated guess to solve the reptile's problem. Example: If the island of Komodo protects its national forests, the Komodo dragon will increase in population.
5 Design the experiment.	Think of a way to test your hypothesis. What can you do on a small scale to see if your educated guess to solve the problem will work? Use your imagination to complete the scientific method with your reptile experiment.
6 Test the hypothesis.	What happened during the experiment? How did the experiment work? What results did you get?
7 Analyze the results.	What do your results mean? Was there a positive or negative response or no change?
8 Formulate conclusions.	Was your hypothesis correct? Why or why not?

Section 2

Atmosphere

You cannot see it, touch it or taste it, but you can feel our atmosphere all around us. It is the wind on our faces and the warmth or coldness we feel. It determines our weather and climate.

Meteorology is the study of Earth's atmosphere and the weather and related events that occur within it. It was not an official science until the 17th century and scientists have been gathering data to predict the weather since the mid-1800s. Today, weather and climate information is gathered using computers, satellites, and radars, as well as ancient weather tools like rain gauges, wind vanes, and the most simple of all, windows.

This section on the atmosphere presents critical thinking questions for students to search the Internet for answers.

Websites for whole class instruction:
http://video.nationalgeographic.com/video/kids/forces-of-nature-kids/weather-101-kids/

http://www.education.noaa.gov/sweather.html

http://www.nws.noaa.gov/om/edures.shtml

http://www.weather.gov/education

http://education.nationalgeographic.com/education/topics/weather/?ar_a=1

Climate

 Use the **key words** in each question to find the answers on the Internet.

1. What is the difference between weather and climate?

_____

_____

_____

2. What are the five climate zones of Mount Kilimanjaro?

Top most: _____ Arctic

Upper portion: _____

Mid portion: _____

Lower portion: _____

Bottom most: _____

3. What effect does elevation have on climate?

_____

_____

_____

4. Where is the world's largest rain forest located?

   _____

5. Why are the hottest climates near the equator?

   _____

   _____

   _____

6. **CHALLENGE** How does climate affect weather? Research the climate and weather of different continents. Use the chart to record your findings.

Area	Climate	Possible Weather
North Africa		
Central America		
Europe		

For questions 7-10, go to http://www.epa.gov/climatestudents/impacts/index.html to visit the *Environmental Protection Agency*'s **website** on climate.

7. What are three signs and impacts of global climate change?

Sign	Impact	Sign	Impact	Sign	Impact
_____	_____	_____	_____	_____	_____
_____	_____	_____	_____	_____	_____
_____		_____		_____	

 On the EPA website, click on the "Think Like a Scientist" tab at the top of the page. Click on "Examine the clues of climate change."

8. What are the 11 signs of climate change in the activity?

1. _____

2. _____

3. _____

4. _____

5. _____

6. _____

7. _____

8. _____

9. _____

10. _____

11. _____

On the EPA website, click on "Take a Climate Change Expedition."

9. Visit three flags on the map to research possible effects of climate change around the world. Use the chart to record your findings.

Flag Location 1	Flag Location 2	Flag Location 3

Effect of Climate Change 1	Effect of Climate Change 1	Effect of Climate Change 1

Effect of Climate Change 2	Effect of Climate Change 2	Effect of Climate Change 2

Effect of Climate Change 3	Effect of Climate Change 3	Effect of Climate Change 3

10. Based on your research, explain possible effects of climate change on Earth on a separate piece of paper.

Clouds

 Use the **key words** in each question to find the answers on the Internet.

1. Clouds are classified into a system using Latin words to describe their appearance from the ground. Use the chart to record these Latin words and their meanings.

Latin Root	Translation	Describes
cumulo cumulus		shape
	"layer"	
	"lock of hair" and "high"	shape and height
		height
	"rain"	

2. What clouds are dark and low-level with light to moderate precipitation?

_____

3. What is the most common form of high-level clouds, which are composed mainly of ice crystals?

_____

4. ![CHALLENGE] Names for clouds are created by combining two Latin roots. Using the Latin roots above, name three clouds. Explain what the cloud name means and describe the weather it produces.

Latin Root	+	Latin Root	=	Cloud Name

Meaning	Weather it Produces

Latin Root	+	Latin Root	=	Cloud Name

Meaning	Weather it Produces

Latin Root	+	Latin Root	=	Cloud Name

Meaning	Weather it Produces

![computer icon] For questions 5-6, visit http://www.weatherwizkids.com/weather-clouds.htm to see the *Weather Wiz Kids* **website** about clouds.

5. Why do small clouds appear white and large clouds appear gray?

_____

_____

_____

_____

_____

6. A cumulonimbus cloud is the most dangerous type of cloud. Explain three reasons why this is true.

_____

_____

_____

For questions 7-12, go to http://eo.ucar.edu/webweather/cloud2.html to see the *Web Weather for Kids* **website** to discover how clouds form.

7. What is the difference between evaporation and condensation?

Evaporation is when …		Condensation is when …
	but	
	but	

On the *Web Weather for Kids* website, click the link to see the **interactive animation** about how temperature affects molecules.

8. Why is there a higher possibility of afternoon rainstorms on a hot day at the beach?

_____

_____

_____

_____

9. Click "Create a portable cloud!" What must be present for clouds to form?

_____   _____   _____

On the *Web Weather for Kids* website, scroll to the bottom and click "Stories."

10. How do clouds affect people?

	Story 1	Story 2	Story 3
Story Title			
Type of Cloud			
Effects on People			

11. Based on the stories you read, summarize ways that clouds affect people.

_____

_____

_____

On the *Web Weather for Kids* website, scroll to the bottom and click "Games" to play the cloud matching **game**.

12. Draw and label a picture of each type of cloud in the matching game.

Precipitation

 Use the **key words** in each question to find the answers on the Internet.

1. Name the four types of precipitation.

   _____   _____   _____   _____

2. Why is rain the most common type of precipitation in a warm, humid climate?

   _____

   _____

3. How many inches of snow fell in Denver, Colorado, in 1999?

   _____

4. Use the Venn diagram to list the differences and similarities of freezing rain and sleet.

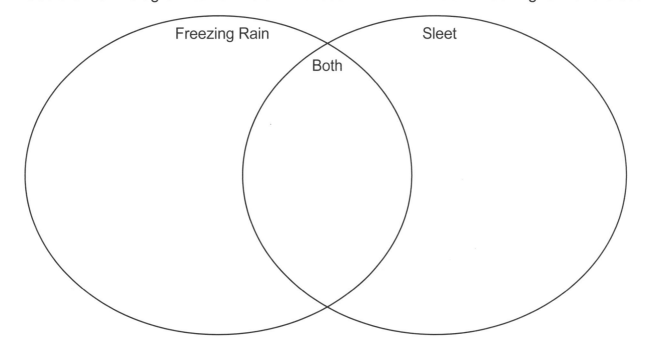

Go to http://www.epa.gov/safewater/kids/flash/flash_watercycle.html and watch the **animation** to study Earth's water cycle.

5. Read the explanation of each phase as it happens. Use the words in the choice box to label the water cycle.

precipitation	aquifer	condensation	clouds	evaporation
vapor	transpiration		water storage	rain

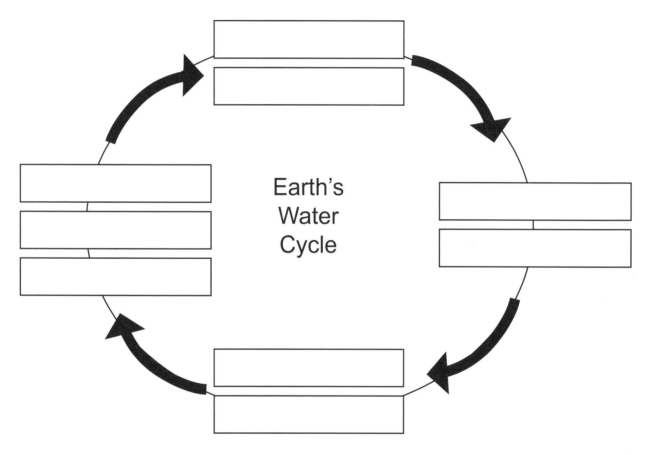

Earth's Water Cycle

Go to http://www.epa.gov/safewater/kids/flash/flash_aquifer.html to "Build Your Own Aquifer" with the **animation**.

6. What does each item in the model represent in nature?

Model	Nature
container	
straw	
white sand	
modeling clay	
small rocks	
green felt	
cocoa	
spray bottle	• •

7. **CHALLENGE** How does nature's underground storage of water work? Use items from the chart to help you write an explanation of Earth's aquifer system.

_____

_____

_____

_____

_____

_____

Go to http://education.nationalgeographic.com/education/encyclopedia/ precipitation/?ar_a=1 to read about precipitation.

8. In what forms is water in the atmosphere visible?

Solid   Liquid   Vapor

| Hail | | Sleet | | Fog | |

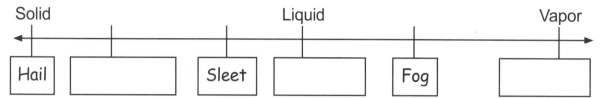 Search the Internet for **images** of the hail formation process.

9.   How does hail form? On a separate piece of paper, draw the process that a raindrop goes through to become hail. Label your diagram using the words in the choice box.

| cloud | raindrops | dust | hail |
| updraft | freezing level | downdraft |

 For questions 10-11, go to http://wateruseitwisely.com/kids/ to play *Water – Use It Wisely's* "Tip Tank" water conservation matching **game**.

10. Use the chart to record your findings about how you can help to save water.

Device	How it Works

11. Choose one of the water-saving devices and write a paragraph persuading a friend to use it to help save water. Tell your friend how it works and why it is important to do this.

_____

_____

_____

_____

For questions 12-14, go to http://ga.water.usgs.gov/edu/msac.html to visit the *USGS Water Science School* **website**.

12. Click on the Challenge Question "How many baths can you get from a rainstorm?" How many baths can you get from 2 inches of rainfall in a 50 x 50 square feet area?

_____

13. Click on the Opinion Survey "Water Shortage! How would you fix it?"

a. Which solution did you think was the best idea? _____

b. In all the United States, which solution has the most popular total? _____

c. What did the rest of the world think the was best? _____

14. Click on the Questionnaire "What is your daily home water use?" and enter your information to determine your daily indoor water use.

_____ gallons per day

15. How would your home water use be different if you had to carry each gallon from a community watering well a mile from your home? Describe ways you would cut back to use less water.

_____

_____

_____

Severe Weather

Use the **key words** in each question to find the answers on the Internet.

1. Which types of thunderstorms produce tornadoes?

   _____   _____

2. What is the difference between a storm watch and a storm warning?

   _____

3. What are the stages and wind speeds of tropical storms?

Tropical Storm Development

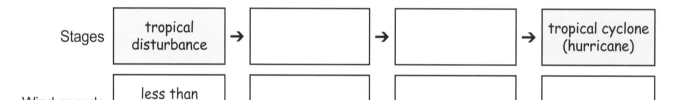

Stages	tropical disturbance	→		→		→	tropical cyclone (hurricane)
Wind speeds	less than 32 mph						

4. Which types of storms are named? _____

5. CHALLENGE What are three retired names that will never be used again? List factors that made that storm significant. (Factors may include damages, death tolls, location, duration, effects on society, effects on science, etc.)

Retired Name	Why

6. What kinds of severe weather occur in North America? Use the chart to list examples.

Spring	Summer	Fall	Winter

  Go to http://www.uwf.edu/atc/projects/coriolis/main.swf and learn about the Coriolis effect and air circulation on Earth. Watch "The Coriolis Effect Defined," "Warm Air Rises…" and "Putting It All Together." Then, take the **quiz**.

7. What is the Coriolis Effect?

_____

_____

For questions 8-12, go to http://science.howstuffworks.com/nature/climate-weather/atmospheric/barometer.htm to use the information about the importance of barometers.

8. What does a barometer measure?

_____

9. Which would most likely have lower air pressure: tropical or polar regions? Why?

_____

_____

_____

10. What kind of weather can you expect in a low-pressure area?

_____

On the *HowStuffWorks* website, click to view the "Storm Chasers: Tornado Aftermath" **video** at the bottom of the page.

11. What size tornado destroyed much of the town of Greensburg, Kansas?

_____

12. Describe the destruction caused by this size tornado.

_____

_____

_____

_____

_____

Go to http://www.youngmeteorologist.org to play *PLAN!T NOW*'s "Severe Weather Preparedness Adventure" **game**.

13. Complete the table with tips for surviving severe weather.

Hurricane Survival Tips	Lightning Survival Tips	Flooding Survival Tips	Tornado Survival Tips	Winter Storm Survival Tips

14. To be prepared for all types of severe weather, what items should be kept in your home?

_____

_____

Weather Instruments

 Use the **key words** in each question to find the answers on the Internet.

1. When were the rain gauge, weather vane, and thermometer invented?

_____   _____   _____

       50 BC   AD 1441   AD 1593

Which is the oldest weather instrument?   _____

2. Where and when was the Tower of the Winds built?

_____

3. What does a sling psychrometer measure?

_____

4. Label the temperatures on these thermometers.

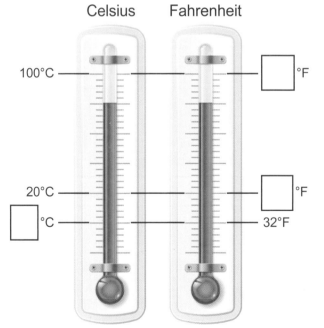

5. What happens when the air around the tube heats up?

_____

_____

6. What happens when the air around the tube cools down?

_____

_____

7. What weather instrument uses photography?

_____

8. **CHALLENGE** "What am I?" Read the clues to identify the correct weather instrument.

Clue	Weather Instrument
To get a proper reading, I should be 5 feet above the ground under a shelter.	
I usually measure between 28 and 31 inches of mercury.	
I am made of two thermometers (one has a wet cloth on the end).	
I have several cups that catch the wind and spin around a pole.	

For questions 9-11, go to http://www.fi.edu/weather/todo/ to the *Franklin Institute*'s "Make Your Own Weather Station" **website**.

9. Which weather station would you most like to build? Why?

_____

_____

10. Which tool would be the easiest to build?

_____

11. Which handmade tools will really measure weather?

_____

_____

_____

Go to http://scijinks.jpl.nasa.gov/wild-weather-adventure and play the "Wild Weather Adventure!" **game**. Guide a weather research blimp and explore Earth's weather for NASA.

12. As you play the "Wild Weather Adventure!" game, keep a record of places your weather blimp stops and the type of weather it encounters there.

Locations	Weather Events

13. ⛰️ CHALLENGE Write about traveling around the world in a weather blimp. Use your imagination to describe your trip. Include at least three weather events and three locations you encountered in the game.

_____

_____

_____

_____

_____

_____

_____

_____

_____

Weather Forecasts

Use the **key words** in each question to find the answers on the Internet.

1. Each type of weather forecast map shows different information. Find what information each map shows and the units of measurement used.

Type of Map	Information Shown	Measurements Used
Pressure	•	• millibar
Temperature	•	•
Station Model	• air pressure • •	• • •
Aviation	• • •	• miles per hour • •
Streamline	•	•

2. Land and ocean geographical features affect weather. What weather is associated with each type of tropical and polar air mass?

Types of Air Masses

		Tropical (hot low pressure)	Polar (cold high pressure)
Geographical Features	Maritime (humid ocean)	mT humid, warm, rainy	
	Continental (dry land)		

Go to http://pbskids.org/dragonflytv/show/forecasting.html to watch a *PBS Kids* **video** about using folklore to forecast the weather.

3. Which ways to predict weather were reliable, and which ways were unreliable?

Reliable Predictors	Unreliable Predictors

Go to http://www.loc.gov/rr/scitech/mysteries/weather-sailor.html to the *Library of Congress* **website** to read about "Everyday Mysteries."

4. Why was the color of the sky at sunrise and sunset the most accurate predictor of the next day's weather?

_____

_____

_____

For questions 5-7, go to http://www.weatherwizkids.com/weather-forecasting.htm
to *Weather Wiz Kids'* "Weather Forecasting" **website** to learn about map symbols.

5. Create your own weather forecast map. Label air masses on the map below using the following weather symbols.

Cold Front (blue)	Warm Front (red)	Stationary Front (red and blue)	Occluded Front (purple)	Trough (black)

6. What determines if a front is labeled cold front or warm front?

_____

_____

7. What kinds of weather occur when a cold air mass meets a warm air mass?

_____

_____

_____

For questions 8-10, go to http://www.weather.com/travel/trip-planner to use *The Weather Channel*'s weather map to plan a road trip to another part of the country.

8.   Use the chart to help you plan your trip.

Destinations: Where are you traveling?

Ⓐ Departure City	Ⓑ Stopping Point 1	Ⓒ Stopping Point 2	Ⓓ Final Destination

Weather: What is the predicted weather forecast along the way?

date				
high temp.				
low temp.				
chance of rain				
cloud cover				

Travel Plan: Click "Get Directions" and you will be taken to Google Maps (maps.google.com). How long will your trip be?

	Ⓐ → Ⓑ		Ⓑ → Ⓒ		Ⓒ → Ⓓ		total distance
miles		+		+		=	
time							

9. List five items you should pack to prepare for the weather in these four cities. Why will each item be necessary?

"I am bringing …	because …"

10. Write a persuasive letter to friend. Ask your friend to come with you on your trip. Describe the places you plan to visit and the weather predicted. Include suggestions for things to bring and activities to do based on the forecasted weather. Use the correct friendly letter format.

Dear _____,

_____

_____

_____

_____

_____

_____

_____

_____

_____

Your friend,

_____

Winds

🔍 Use the **key words** in each question to find the answers on the Internet.

1. Which direction does a katabatic wind blow? What does "katabatic" mean in Greek?

   _____

   _____

2. Complete the wind name chart below.

Wind Name	Location	Name Translation
bora (bura)		
Bohemian wind		
mistral		
Santa Ana		
tramontane		
Oroshi		

3. How did a Chinook wind affect the weather in Montana in 1900?

   _____

   _____

4. Where does the sirocco wind originate?

   _____

5. What type of land forms in the horse latitudes?

   _____

Search the Internet for **images** of air patterns.

6. Label each air pattern and line of latitude on the map. Use arrows to show the direction(s) each air pattern goes.

<u>Air Patterns</u>
Trade Winds
Polar Easterlies
Westerlies
Doldrums

<u>Lines of Latitude</u>
Tropic of Cancer
Tropic of Capricorn
Horse Latitudes
Arctic Circle
Antarctic Circle
Equator

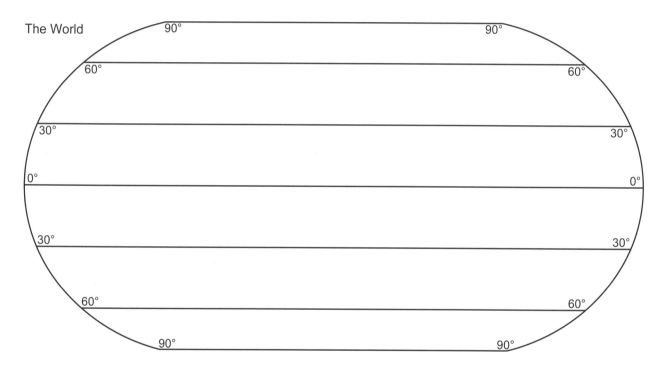

The World

Go to http://www.bbc.co.uk/schools/whatisweather/aboutweather/windforce.shtml and watch the **animations** of different wind forces.

7. Why is it difficult to fly a kite on a calm day?

_____

_____

For questions 8-10, go to http://www.windfinder.com to explore the interactive "Wind Forecast Map Worldwide."
- Type the name of your town or a large city nearest you to find a weather station.
- Choose a weather station and select "Forecast."

8. What is the current weather?

Air Temperature	Wind Speed

9. What is the forecast for tomorrow's weather?

	Air Temperature	Wind Speed
High		
Low		

10. Click on the ✎ Maps tab to view wind direction. What is the prevalent (or main) direction of the wind in your area?

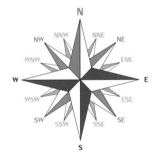

11. On a separate piece of paper, create a short story about a day playing outside when the weather changes from moderate to gale force winds. Describe how the wind change affects your family or friends and your things. Use the chart to plan your story.

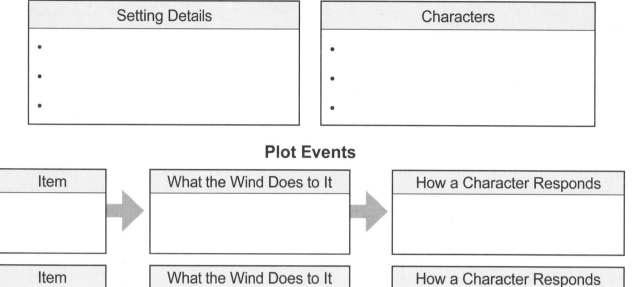

Introduction

Setting Details	Characters
• • •	• • •

Plot Events

Item	What the Wind Does to It	How a Character Responds

Item	What the Wind Does to It	How a Character Responds

Item	What the Wind Does to It	How a Character Responds

Conclusion

One thing I learned in the wind that day …

12. Illustrate the beginning and the ending of your story.

Moderate Wind	Gale Wind

Section 3

Ecosystems and Habitats

Many forms of life call Earth home. All living things must share our planet's resources, such as food, water, air and living space. Consequently, we are all connected in complex ways. Ecology is the study of how living things and their environment affect each other.

Environments are as diverse as the living things that inhabit them. All living and nonliving things that exist together in an environment is called an ecosystem. Earth's largest ecosystem is the biosphere, which is the entire region of Earth where all living things can be found. To study the biosphere, scientists divided it into smaller ecosystems called biomes.

This section on ecosystems and habitats presents critical thinking questions for students to search the Internet for answers.

Websites for whole class instruction:
http://education.nationalgeographic.com/education/media/why-ocean-matters/?ar_a=1

http://disney.go.com/disneynature/oceans/

http://education.nationalgeographic.com/education/topics/ecosystems/?ar_a=1

http://education-portal.com/academy/lesson/food-chains-trophic-levels-and-energy-flow-
    in-an-ecosystem.html

Deserts

 Use the **key words** in each question to find the answers on the Internet.

1. 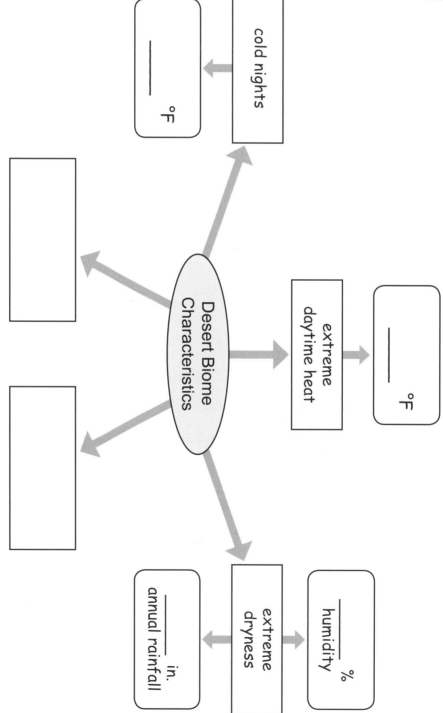 What are characteristics of a desert biome? Use the graphic organizer to record your findings.

cold nights

_____ °F

Desert Biome Characteristics

extreme daytime heat

_____ °F

extreme dryness

_____ in. annual rainfall

_____ % humidity

2. On average, how many more inches of rain fall in the rain forest than in the desert annually?

rain forest		desert		
	−		=	

inches of rainfall per year

3. Name Earth's largest desert. Where is it located?

_____

4. Deserts are usually found between which lines of latitude?

_____

 Go to http://www.neok12.com/diagram/Deserts-01.htm to the *NeoK12* **website** to "Label the Major Deserts of the World."

5. Label the map with the letters of your final answers.

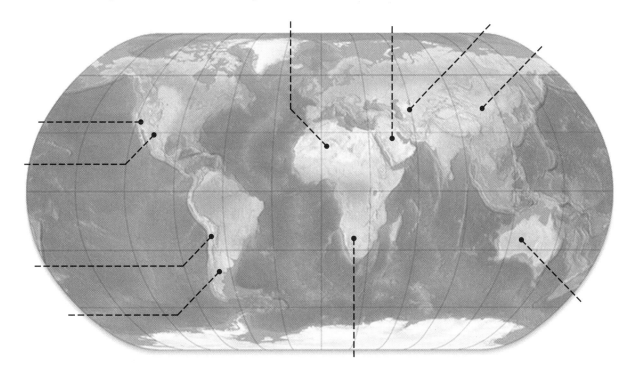

a. Gobi	b. Turkestan	c. Kalahari	d. Arabian	e. Sonoran
f. Sahara	g. Australian	h. Atacama	i. Mojave	j. Patagonian

For questions 6-10, go to http://environment.nationalgeographic.com/environment/ habitats/desert-profile/ to read *National Geographic*'s "Deserts" profile.

6. How much of Earth's land is covered in deserts?

_____

7. What are four adaptations that desert animals use for desert survival? How do these adaptations help to keep the animals thriving?

Adaptation	How it Helps

8. Name two adaptations of desert plants for surviving with less water.

_____   _____

9. 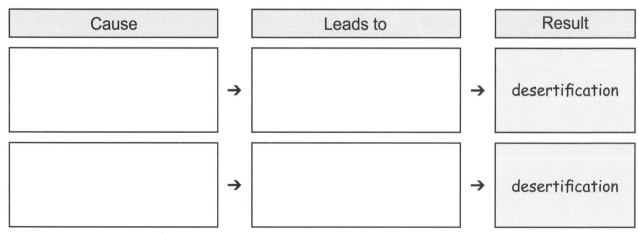 **CHALLENGE** What are two causes of desertification? How do they affect the land? Use the chart to record your findings.

Cause		Leads to		Result
	→		→	desertification
	→		→	desertification

Scroll down to the bottom of the *National Geographic* website and click on "Photo Gallery: Desert Wildlife" to see the 8 **images**.

10. Sort the life forms pictured into these three categories. (Some pictures include examples of more than one category.)

Plants	Animals Living in Herds for Protection	Carnivores (Hunters)
• • • •	• • • •	• • • •

Choose two desert **videos** to watch. Use the Venn diagram on the next page to take notes while watching the videos.

① **Gobi Desert** (5:39)
http://education.nationalgeographic.com/education/media/gobi-desert/?ar_a=1

② **Mali Desert** (3:02)
http://video.nationalgeographic.com/video/places/countries-places/mali/mali_malidesert/

③ **Sahara Desert** (2:38)
http://video.nationalgeographic.com/video/animals/mammals-animals/zebras-horses-camels/camel_dromedary_tunisia/

④ **Sonoran Desert** (5:41)
http://education.nationalgeographic.com/education/media/sonoran-babies/?ar_a=1

11.

_____ Desert   _____ Desert

Both

12. Write a paragraph comparing and contrasting the two deserts. How are they alike? What is unique about each?

_____

_____

_____

_____

_____

_____

_____

_____

Food Webs

 Use the **key words** in each question to find the answers on the Internet.

1. A food chain **producer** is a living organism that manufactures its own food. What are four examples of producers in **North America**?

_____   _____

_____   _____

2. A food chain **consumer** is a living organism that cannot make its own food, so it needs to consume other living organisms. What are four examples of consumers in **Africa**?

_____   _____

_____   _____

3. A food chain **decomposer** is a living organism that eats dead organisms and reduces them to simpler forms of matter. What are four examples of decomposers in **Asia**?

_____   _____

_____   _____

Go to http://www.sheppardsoftware.com/content/animals/kidscorner/games/ animaldietgame.htm to play *Sheppard Software*'s "Animal Diet" **game**.

4. What is the difference between an herbivore's diet and a carnivore's diet? List five foods that belong in each circle. What label belongs in the big rectangle?

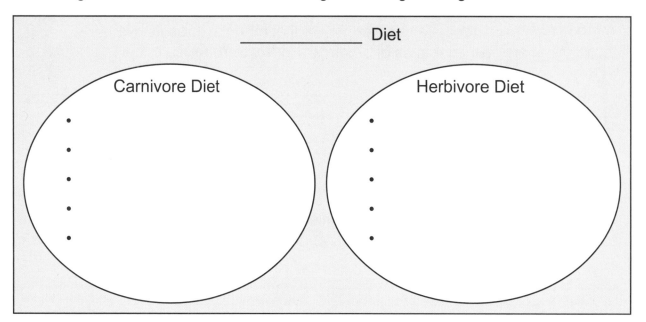

 Go to http://www.sheppardsoftware.com/content/animals/kidscorner/games/ producersconsumersgame.htm to play the "Producer and Consumers" **game**.

5. List five examples of decomposers from the game.

_____ _____ _____

_____ _____

6. Why are decomposers important in nature? (What would happen if nature did not have decomposers?)

_____

_____

_____

_____

_____

_____

A Food Web is formed from all the producers, consumers and decomposers living together in one ecosystem.

 Go to http://www.sheppardsoftware.com/content/animals/kidscorner/games/ foodchaingame.htm to play *Sheppard Software*'s "The Food Chain Game."

7. Draw and label "5. Full chain" with the eagle when you complete it.

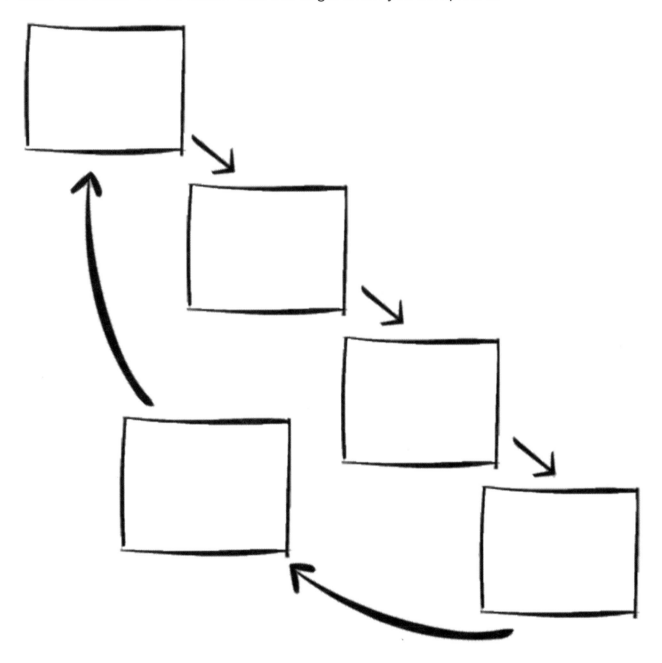

8. Choose a consumer, producer or decomposer that interests you. On a separate piece of paper, write a story about a day in the life of your organism. Describe how it acquires food, what foods or energy sources it uses, and what benefits it provides to the ecosystem.

Forests

 Use the **key words** in each question to find the answers on the Internet.

1. What are characteristics of forests?

	Coniferous Forest	Temperate Deciduous Forest
Definition		
Locations		
Climate		
Animals		

2. All living and nonliving parts of a biome **give** to the ecosystem and **take** from the ecosystem. What do each of these things give and take from their biomes?

Member of Biomes	Bacteria	Water	Green Plant	Bird
Give				
Take				

Go to http://www.americanforests.org/discover-forests/forest-facts/ to see the *American Forests* **website**. Read and discover how forests help the entire Earth.

3. How do forests benefit these specific areas?

Air: _____

_____

Wildlife: _____

_____

People: _____

_____

Energy: _____

_____

Go to http://www.smokeybear.com/kids/default.asp?js=1 to go to "Smokey's Outpost" and play **activities** and **games** to learn about preventing forest fires.

4. On a separate piece of paper, write a thank you letter to Smokey Bear for helping to protect America's forests. Describe the benefits of forest biomes and explain why they should be protected and preserved. Include ways you can prevent forest fires. Use the outline to plan your letter.

Benefits of Forest Biomes

    I. _____

    II. _____

    III. _____

Why Forest Biomes Should Be Protected and Preserved

    I. _____

    II. _____

    III. _____

Ways That I Can Help to Prevent Forest Fires

    I. _____

    II. _____

    III. _____

Go to http://www.scholastic.com/growgreen/virtualforest/ to play *Scholastic*'s "Virtual Forest Challenge" **game** and learn simple ways to help forests grow.

5. For each location in the game, list one choice you can make to conserve energy and save forests.

Location	Choice	Impact
House		
School		
Store		
Park		

6. Write a persuasive letter to a community leader about starting a recycling program. Include the benefits of recycling to help save forests.

_____

_____

_____

_____

_____

_____

_____

_____

_____

_____

_____

_____

Grasslands

 Use the **key words** in each question to find the answers on the Internet.

1. What are characteristics of grassland biomes?

	Temperate Grasslands	Tropical Grasslands (Savannas)
Definition		
Locations		
Climate		
Animals		

2. List the name for grasslands in each of the following areas.

South America: _____

North America: _____

Africa: _____

Eurasia: _____

Go to http://www.watchknowlearn.org/Video.aspx?VideoID=6521&CategoryID=2313 to watch *WatchKnowLearn*'s "History of Migration of Animals in Africa" **video**.

3. How has animal migration affected the plant adaptation in the savanna?

Animal	Migrated From	Effect on the Savanna Biome
giraffe		
antelope		
elephant		

Go to http://www.sheppardsoftware.com/content/animals/quizzes/kidscorner/animal_games_african_sav_large.html to play *Sheppard Software*'s "African Savannah Animals" **game** to identify native wildlife.

4. When the game is over, list three examples for each category.

African Savanna Animals

Mammal	Reptile	Insect	Bird
•	•	•	•
•	•	•	•
•	•	•	•

Go to http://www.bellmuseum.umn.edu/games/prairie/build/index.html to play the Bell Museum's "Build a Prairie" **game**.

5. List four North American shortgrass prairie animals for each category.

North American Shortgrass Prairie Animals

Birds	Mammals	Amphibians and Reptiles (Herps)

Go to http://www.bbc.co.uk/nature/humanplanetexplorer/environments/ grasslands#p00f0xy8 to watch **videos** about adaptation in the grasslands.

6. CHALLENGE How have people adapted their skills, technology, and land to be successful in their grassland biome?

Adaptation Type	Grassland Location	Example of Adaptation
Human Skill		
Technology Use		
Land Use		

7. Describe life in the grasslands of the world. Describe the grasslands and adaptations people have used for survival.

_____

_____

_____

_____

_____

_____

_____

_____

_____

Oceans

 Use the **key words** in each question to find the answers on the Internet.

1. What percentage of the earth is covered with the ocean biome?

   _____

2. Why does 90% of ocean life inhabit the euphotic zone?

   _____

 Go to http://www.windows2universe.org/earth/Water/marine_ecology.html to the *Windows to the Universe* **website** and read about four environments in the ocean biome.

3. Describe each zone's location and list its inhabitants.

	Intertidal Zone	Shallow Ocean	Open Ocean	Deep Ocean
Location				
Inhabitants				

For questions 4-6, go to http://video.nationalgeographic.com/video/environment/ habitats-environment/habitats-oceans-env/coral-reefs/?videoDetect=t%252Ct on the *National Geographic* website and watch the **video** about coral reefs.

4. Name the largest coral reef. Where is it located? How big is it?

_____

_____

5. What predator hunts around a coral reef?

_____

6. What are three threats to the survival of coral reefs?

_____   _____   _____

 For questions 7-9, go to http://ed.ted.com/lessons/deep-ocean-mysteries-and-wonders to watch the "Deep Ocean Mysteries and Wonders" **video**.

7. Create a list of interesting things that scientists have found while exploring 5% of the ocean.

Life	"Land" Formations	"Water" Formations

8. How does bioluminescence help a species in the deep ocean?

_____

_____

9. Why can't the deep ocean animals be collected with a net? (Why can they only
   be photographed?)

_____

_____

_____

_____

Go to http://kids.nationalgeographic.com/kids/activities/new/ocean/ and choose
one sea creature to research by watching the **video** feature.

10. Summarize what you discovered about your creature.

_____

_____

_____

_____

_____

_____

_____

Rain Forests

 Use the **key words** in each question to find the answers on the Internet.

1. What are the characteristics of the rain forest biome?

Rain Forest	
Definition	
Locations	
Climate	
Animals	

 Search the Internet for **images** of the layers of a rain forest.

2. What are the four layers of a rain forest? What type of flora is found in each layer?
Sketch and label your answer.

For questions 3-7, go to http://www.rainforest-alliance.org/multimedia/treehouse to play *Rainforest Alliance*'s "Track it Back" **game** to learn about products that come from the rain forest.

3. How was coffee discovered?

_____

_____

4. What are the 6 steps in producing coffee?

Start
1

| |

2

| |

3

| |

Finish

4

| |

5

| |

6

| |

5. Why is growing coffee in the shade better for the environment?

_____

_____

6. What plant produces chocolate?

_____

7. What are the 8 steps in producing chocolate?

Start
1

| |

2

| |

3

| |

4

| |

Finish

5

| |

6

| |

7

| |

8

| |

Go to http://video.nationalgeographic.com/video/kids/people-places-kids/canada-rainforest-kids/ to watch *National Geographic*'s "Canadian Rain Forest" **video**.

8. Commercial loggers and environmental conservationists view the Canadian temperate rain forest differently. What are their competing goals for the forest?

Canadian Temperate Rain Forest

Commercial Logging Goals	Environmental Conservationist Goals

9. Explain why commercial loggers and environmental conservationists were arguing about the Canadian temperate rain forest. How does the Great Bear Rainforest compromise satisfy both sides?

_____

_____

_____

_____

_____

_____

Go to http://www.bbc.co.uk/nature/habitats/Tropical_and_subtropical_moist_ broadleaf_forests on the *BBC*'s website to watch **videos**, see **images**, and read **articles** about rain forest flora and fauna.

10. Scroll down to "What grows here?" Choose a plant that grows only in the rain forest and describe two of its unusual characteristics.

_____

_____

11. **CHALLENGE** Scroll down to "What lives here?" Analyze the fauna of the rain forest to discover five animals that are found only in rain forests. Click on an animal's picture to go to its page and then scroll to the habitat section to find out where else it might live. Complete the chart about five animals.

Animals Found Only in Rain Forests

Animal Name	Location (Country)	Behaviors	Endangered Status

Go to http://video.nationalgeographic.com/video/kids/people-places-kids/costa-rica-dest-kids/ to watch *National Geographic*'s **video** "Destination: Costa Rica."

12. Plan your own imaginary vacation to Costa Rica's rain forest.

Costa Rican Rain Forest Vacation

When to Go	
Activities to Do	Animals to See
•	•
•	•
•	•
•	•
•	•

13. Write a story describing your trip. Use sensory details and dialog while describing encounters in your narrative.

_____

_____

_____

_____

_____

_____

_____

_____

_____

Taiga and Tundra

 Use the **key words** in each question to find the answers on the Internet.

1. What are characteristics of the taiga and tundra biomes?

	Taiga	Tundra
Definition		
Locations		
Climate		
Animals		

2. What are two main differences between the taiga and tundra biomes?

_____

_____

3. How does permafrost prevent many forms of plant life in the tundra?

_____

_____

_____

Go to http://dsc.discovery.com/tv-shows/other-shows/videos/assignment-discovery-shorts-iii-biomes-taiga.htm to watch a *Discovery* **video** about the taiga.

4. How are coniferous trees adapted to the taiga's cold climate?

_____

_____

5. Describe three adaptations of mammals for surviving the taiga's winters.

_____

_____

_____

 Go to http://dsc.discovery.com/tv-shows/other-shows/videos/assignment-discovery-shorts-iii-biomes-tundra.htm to watch a *Discovery* **video** about the tundra.

6. How are year-round inhabitants of the tundra similar?

_____

7. Describe two adaptations of animals living in the tundra.

_____

_____

 Imagine you are standing at the demarcation or tree line between the taiga and the tundra biomes. What do you see? Use an **image** search to find ideas.

8. **CHALLENGE** On a separate piece of paper, draw a picture of the taiga to the south and the tundra to the north of the tree line. Include animals and plants in each biome. What time of year is it? Color your picture to reflect either the winter season or the summer season.

9. **CHALLENGE** On a separate piece of paper, write a narrative story about a child who lives in the place you illustrated. How does the ecosystem affect the child's life? Include dialog and sensory details about the surroundings.

Section 4

Energy

Energy is everywhere. It is in everything we do and is needed by everything we use. There are two basic kinds of energy: stored (potential) and working (kinetic); and two basic kinds of energy sources: renewable and non-renewable.

Earth's main source of energy is the sun. Without the sun's light energy, Earth would cease to exist. However, solar energy accounts for less than 6% of electricity produced in the United States. Scientists are working to increase this percentage.

This section on energy presents critical thinking questions for students to search the Internet for answers.

Websites for whole class instruction:
http://energy.gov/science-innovation/science-education

http://video.pbs.org/video/1095269427/ (fossil fuels)

http://education.nationalgeographic.com/education/activity/geography-oil-drilling-gulf-mexico/?ar_a=1

http://video.pbs.org/video/980039287/ (solar power)

http://www.eia.gov/kids/

Experiment with wind and solar power by conducting these experiments:
http://www.sciencekids.co.nz/videos/physics/windenergy.html
http://www1.eere.energy.gov/kids/roofus/pizza_box.html
http://www1.eere.energy.gov/kids/roofus/sundial.html

Electromagnetism

Use the **key words** in each question to find the answers on the Internet.

1. What are the four basic forces in the universe?

_____   _____

_____   _____

2. Which force is at work in motors and generators?

_____

3. Which tiny particles within an atom have an electrical charge?

_____   _____

4. Ions are positively or negatively charged atoms. What is the difference between a positively charged atom and a negatively charged atom?

Positively Charged Atom (Cation)	Negatively Charged Atom (Anion)

5. What is an electric current?

_____

6. What is the difference between insulators and conductors?

Insulators	Conductors

For questions 7-9, go to http://video.nationalgeographic.com/video/kids/cartoons-tv-movies-kids/i-didnt-know-that-kids/idkt-magnets-kids/ and watch *National Geographic*'s "Magnets" **video**.

7. What is a magnet?

_____

_____

8. How does the first rule of magnetism relate to a compass?

_____

_____

9. How are magnets used to stop an amusement park ride?

_____

_____

_____

 For questions 10-13, go to http://www.tvakids.com/PB_08/index.html to learn about electromagnetism with the "Power Bandit Tracker." Watch the **videos** in "Get the Basics."

10. What role do electrons play in electricity? (Watch "Basics of Electrons.")

_____

_____

11. How does an object become magnetized? (Watch "Basics of Magnetism.")

_____

_____

12. Which machine produces electric current? (Watch "Electricity: Moving Electrons.")

_____

13. How does a motor convert electrical energy into mechanical energy?

_____

_____

_____

_____

_____

🎮 Go to http://www.bbc.co.uk/schools/scienceclips/ages/10_11/changing_circuits .shtml and play the "Changing Circuits" **game**. Click the top arrows to try all changes to the circuit.

14. Why does a light bulb become brighter when voltage is increased?

_____

_____

15. Why does a light bulb become dimmer when the length of wire is increased?

_____

_____

🎮 Go to http://www.engineeringinteract.org/resources/siliconspies/flash/concepts/ buildingcircuits.htm to learn about symbols used to draw electric circuits in the "Building Circuits" **game**.

16. Draw the symbol for each component.

battery	motor	buzzer	connector	open switch

17. Practice building circuits in the game. Then draw a closed circuit with a battery and a motor that sounds a buzzer when the switch is closed.

Energy and Conservation

🔍 Use the **key words** in each question to find the answers on the Internet.

1. Define energy.

   _____

   _____

2. Name and describe the two main types of energy.

   _____

   _____

   _____

3. Describe forms of energy.

Form of Energy	Characteristics	Example
Thermal (Heat) Energy		
Chemical Energy		
Electrical Energy		
Sound Energy		

4. Heat energy is transmitted through conduction, convection, or radiation. Write a paragraph explaining how popcorn can be made using each transmission of heat. Use the chart to take notes about the types of energy transmissions before writing your paragraph.

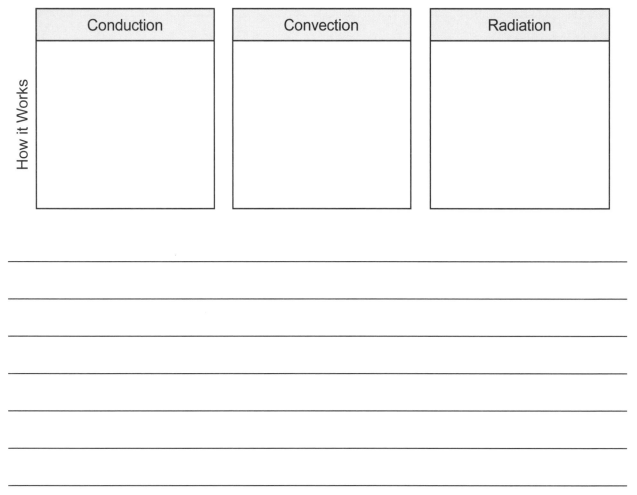

Conduction	Convection	Radiation

How it Works

_____

_____

_____

_____

_____

_____

_____

 Search the Internet for **images** of the five sources of renewable energy listed below.

5. ⛰ CHALLENGE On a separate piece of paper, illustrate five sources of renewable energy demonstrating how each is renewed.

biomass	geothermal	hydropower	solar	wind

Go to http://www.neok12.com/php/watch.php?v=zX0a7f7a41717c595f787f0a&t=Law-of-Conservation to watch the "Bowling Ball – Conservation of Energy" **video**.

6. How does the bowling ball use potential and kinetic energy? Explain how the Law of Conservation of Energy controls the bowling ball.

_____

_____

_____

_____

For questions 7-9, go to http://www.energystar.gov/index.cfm?c=kids.kids_index to see the *Energy Star Kids* **website** and read about conserving energy.

7. What is energy conservation?

_____

_____

8. Name three consequences that could happen if we use too much energy.

_____ _____ _____

9. Click on the "You Can Make Big Changes" tab at the bottom of the page. What are five changes you can make to help conserve energy? Why are these changes helpful?

Change	How it Conserves Energy

Fossil Fuels

 Use the **key words** in each question to find the answers on the Internet.

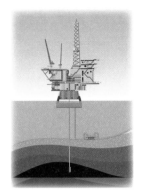

1. How were fossil fuels formed?

   _____

   _____

2. What are the three basic types of fossil fuels?

   _____   _____   _____

   Draw a ★ next to the two that were created the same way.

3. How does the use of fossil fuels impact the environment?

Fossil Fuels	Oil	Coal	Natural Gas
Impact From **Extracting** From Earth			
Impact From **Burning** for Energy			

4. Name five products made from oil.

   _____   _____   _____

   _____   _____

5. Why are fossil fuels the number one energy source used?

   _____

   _____

Go to http://www.watchknowlearn.org/Video.aspx?VideoID=30456 to watch *WatchKnowLearn*'s "Thermal Electricity – How It Works" **video**.

6. How does a factory convert the energy from burning coal to electricity?

Step	Location	Function
1	coal yard	
2	conveyor belt	
3	pulverizer	
4	furnace	
5	boiler tubes	
6	large pipes	
7	turbine	
8	generator rotor	
9	stator	
10	transformers	
11	power lines	

Go to http://teachertube.com/viewVideo.php?video_id=77641&title=Fossil_Fuels_with_Bill_Nye and watch the "Fossil Fuels with Bill Nye" **video**.

7. How have the oil and coal industries adapted to the increased need for fossil fuels?

	Coal	Oil
New Methods of **Removing** the Fossil Fuel		
How it Works		

8. CHALLENGE Explain the new advances in finding and extracting fossil fuels. What are the benefits and disadvantages of obtaining more fossil fuels?

_____

_____

_____

_____

_____

_____

_____

_____

_____

_____

Hydroelectricity

 Use the key words in each question to find the answers on the Internet.

1. What is hydroelectricity? Is it renewable?

   _____

   _____

   _____

2. How do hydroelectric power plant managers plan for peak periods for power on a hot summer day?

   _____

   _____

3. What is the name of the largest capacity hydroelectric power plant **in the world** and where is it located?

Name	Location

4. What is the name of the largest capacity hydroelectric power plant **in the USA** and where is it located?

Name	Location

Go to http://www.eia.gov/state/?sid to the *U.S. Energy Information Administration*'s map to use the **interactive map**.

5. What is the closest hydroelectric power plant to your school?

Name	Location

Go to http://ga.water.usgs.gov/edu/hyhowworks.html to *The USGS Water Science School*'s "Hydroelectric Power: How it Works" **website**.

6. **CHALLENGE** How does hydroelectric power work? Use the words below to draw and label a diagram to explain.

generator	intake	penstock	powerhouse
power lines	reservoir	turbine	outflow

7. **CHALLENGE** Describe the seven sequential steps in transmitting power from a hydroelectric dam to a home.

_____

_____

_____

_____

_____

_____

_____

Go to http://www.usbr.gov/lc/hooverdam/educate/kidfacts.html to the *U.S. Department of the Interior*'s **website** and read "Hoover Dam Factoids for Kids."

8. Complete the table.

Hoover Dam Facts

Main Construction Material Used	River Feeding the Dam
Years Construction Began and Completed	Number of Generators
Height	Power Capacity – Number of Households

Go to http://www.hydroquebec.com/games/network/flash.html to the *Hydro Quebéc* **website** to build a hydroelectric power system.

9. What is the difference between a transmission substation and a distribution station in a hydroelectric grid?

Transmission Substation	Distribution Station

Nuclear Energy

 Use the **key words** in each question to find the answers on the Internet.

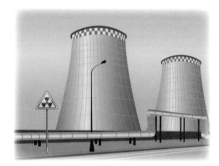

1. What are the differences between nuclear fusion and nuclear fission?

	Nuclear Fusion	Nuclear Fission
How is the energy released?		
What uses this process to produce energy?		

2. What is the function of a nuclear reactor?

_____

_____

3. What is an isotope? What are some health risks and uses of uranium isotopes?

Isotope Definition	
Health Risks Linked to Uranium Isotopes	Uses for Uranium Isotopes

4. Approximately what percent of electricity production in the United States is from nuclear energy?

_____

5. What was the first use of nuclear energy?

_____

6. Nuclear power has been extremely controversial since its first use. Research the positives and negatives associated with nuclear energy.

Nuclear Energy Pros	Nuclear Energy Cons
• • • 	• • •

7. Based on your research, do you think nuclear power should be used as a source of energy? Why or why not?

_____

_____

_____

_____

_____

_____

_____

_____

Go to http://www.opg.com/power/nuclear/howitworks.asp to watch the *Ontario Power Generation* "How Nuclear Power Works" **video**.

8. Draw and label a diagram of a nuclear power plant.

9. What are the basic steps in the nuclear power plant cycle to generate electricity from nuclear fission?

1.	
2.	
3.	
4.	
5.	
6.	
7.	

Go to http://www.npr.org/2011/03/17/134568383/japan-three-mile-island-chernobyl-putting-it-all-in-perspective to read *NPR*'s "Fukushima, Three Mile Island, Chernobyl: Putting It All In Perspective" **article**.

10. Compare the three nuclear disasters.

Nuclear Meltdowns

Three Mile Island	Chernobyl	Fukushima

11. What are the main differences between the three disasters? Describe an action that builders or workers could have taken to prevent the severity of each incident.

_____

_____

_____

_____

_____

_____

_____

Go to http://www.nuclearpowersimulator.com/ to use the "Nuclear Power Plant Simulator" **game**. Can you control fission to produce electricity? Can you prevent a nuclear meltdown?

There are directions on the simulator's website, but the VERY basic directions are:

- Click on center on simulator to see the nuclear power plant's control board.

- Click on start/reset at bottom of control board to begin simulator.

- Click on primary pump and secondary pump first.

- Click the + on reactor core to raise the control rods and begin the fission process of releasing energy.

- Click the + on pri coolant and sec coolant to control the temperatures in the reactor core and the heat exchanger. (Do not exceed max temps!)

- **CHALLENGE** Continue increasing the level of the reactor core and pri/sec coolants to release as much nuclear energy to heat the water without going over maximum temperatures.

12. How do you cool the reactor core if it gets too hot?

_____

_____

13. Evaluate the simulator.

a. What did you like about the nuclear power simulator?

_____

_____

b. What did you dislike about the nuclear power simulator?

_____

_____

c. What did the simulator help you understand about a nuclear power plant?

_____

_____

Solar and Wind Energy

 Use the **key words** in each question to find the answers on the Internet.

1.

	Solar Energy	Wind Power
Definition		
Largest "Farm" in the World and its Location		

2. **CHALLENGE** How do wind turbines work? Use words from the choice box in your explanation.

wind	lift	rotate	drive shaft	generator	electricity

_____

_____

_____

_____

_____

For questions 3-5, go to http://www.eia.gov/kids/energy.cfm?page=solar_home-basics and use key word searches to find answers in "Solar Basics."

3. What are three common uses for solar energy?

_____   _____   _____

4. How do photovoltaic cells convert sunlight into energy?

_____

_____

_____

5. **CHALLENGE** Describe how solar energy is used to make steam. How is the steam then used?

_____

_____

_____

On the Energy Kids website, click on "Wind" from the list of energy sources.

6. What are good locations for a wind farm?

_____   _____

_____   _____

Go to http://videos.howstuffworks.com/howstuffworks/51308-stuff-to-blow-your-kids-mind-solar-power-video.htm to watch the *HowStuffWorks* "Solar Power" **video**.

7. Light colors <u>reflect</u> heat and dark colors <u>absorb</u> heat. How can we use this information about solar energy to reduce energy consumption?

_____

_____

_____

_____

Go to http://video.nationalgeographic.com/video/environment/energy-environment/ solar-power/ to watch the *National Geographic* "Energy: Solar Power" **video**.

8. What are some benefits of using solar panels?

 Go to http://video.nationalgeographic.com/video/environment/energy-environment/ wind-power/ to watch the *National Geographic* "Energy: Iowa Wind Power" **video**.

9. What are some benefits of using wind energy?

 Go to http://www.time.com/time/video/player/0,32068,27456914001_1907002,00 .html to watch *TIME*'s "The Truth About Wind Power" **video**.

10. What are some of the problems with using wind energy?

11. CHALLENGE Pretend your school or home is considering building a wind turbine. Think about the pros (benefits) and cons (problems) of wind energy listed above. Think about your school or home's location compared to the best geography for a wind turbine.

Decide if wind energy would benefit your school or home. On a separate piece of paper, explain why or why not.

Section 5

Geology

Earth is a very unique place. It is the only planet known to support life. Geology is the study of Earth and constant changes it undergoes. Earth consists of four layers: the inner core, the outer core, the mantle, and the crust.

Most of Earth's action takes place on the moving crust. The main component of the crust is rock and rocks are made of minerals. The crust is in constant movement due to plate tectonics and the volatile mantel layer beneath the crust. These two forces cause violent change through volcanoes and earthquakes. However, most of Earth experiences slow change through erosion and weathering.

This section on geology presents critical thinking questions for students to search the Internet for answers.

Websites for whole class instruction:

http://videos.howstuffworks.com/discovery/31883-howstuffworks-show-episode-4-power-of-water-erosion-video.htm

http://www.sdnhm.org/archive/kids/minerals/collection1.html

http://www.learner.org/interactives/dynamicearth/plate2.html

http://www.heritagekids.info/school/Science/Plate%20Tectonic%20Game%20Show%20Flash.html

http://video.nationalgeographic.com/video/kids/forces-of-nature-kids/volcanoes-101-kids/

www.youtube.com/watch?v=3HQwYbwmyaY

Erosion and Weathering

 Use the **key words** in each question to find the answers on the Internet.

1. What is erosion?

   _____

   _____

   _____

2. What begins the erosion process?

   _____

3. What is the term for solid organic matter transported by wind, water, or glacial erosion?

   _____

4. Which river created the Grand Canyon?

   _____

For questions 5-9, go to http://www.unitedstreaming.com/videos/dsc/external Applications/interactiveVideos/index.html?vid=32 to watch *Discovery Science*'s "Weathering and Erosion" **interactive video**.

5. Take notes about chemical and mechanical weathering while interacting with the video.

Weathering
Definition

| Chemical | | Mechanical |

| Definition | | Definition |

| Examples | | Examples |

6. How is rust (iron oxide) created?

_____

7. What chemical weathering agent does acid rain contain?

_____

8. How is sand created?

_____

_____

9. How does clear cutting land increase erosion?

_____

Glacial weathering forms impressive landscape features. Locate an **image** on the Internet that shows landscape formed by glacial weathering and erosion.

10. Sketch your favorite glacial-formed landscape image here.

11. Imagine you lived in the landscape above. Write a creative story about life in this transformative place. How much would the geography affect your life?

Ways the Geography Affects My Life

_____

_____

_____

_____

_____

_____

_____

Go to http://www.glencoe.com/sites/common_assets/science/virtual_labs/ES08/ ES08.html to use *Glencoe*'s erosion **experiment**. Follow steps 1-7 in the procedure.

12. a. What is your hypothesis statement (educated guess about what will happen in the experiment)?

_____

_____

Slope Gradient (degrees)	Vegetation?	Rain Intensity	Sediment Level	↑↓
30°	Yes	Low	3	

Which settings caused the most and least amounts of sediment in the runoff? Put a ↑ beside the highest sediment level and a ↓ beside the lowest sediment level in the far right column.

b. Was your hypothesis correct? _____

c. What can you conclude about erosion from the virtual experiment?

_____

_____

Minerals

🔍 Use the **key words** in each question to find the answers on the Internet.

1. What are minerals?

   _____

   _____

2. How are minerals different from rocks?

   _____

   _____

3. What physical properties are used to identify minerals?

   1. _____   5. _____   9. _____

   2. _____   6. _____   10. _____

   3. _____   7. _____   11. _____

   4. _____   8. _____   12. _____

4. Created in 1812 by German mineralogist Fredrick Mohs, the Mohs Relative Hardness Scale ranks 10 minerals commonly available. Draw, color, and label his 10 minerals from softest (1) to hardest (10).

Mohs Relative Hardness Scale

1. _____	2. _____	3. _____	4. _____	5. _____
6. _____	7. _____	8. _____	9. _____	10. _____

Go to http://www.glencoe.com/sites/common_assets/science/virtual_labs/ES03/ES03.html to use *Glencoe*'s "Identifying Minerals" **virtual lab**.

5. Read about how minerals can be defined by their properties on the left side of the screen. Summarize the five characteristics that all minerals share.

Minerals

1.	
2.	
3.	
4.	
5.	

6. Read the steps of the virtual lab procedure and follow the procedure to identify the mystery minerals.

Mineral "B"

Color	Luster

Hardness	Cleave or Fracture?

What is the mystery mineral's identity?

Go to http://www.oum.ox.ac.uk/thezone/minerals/define/cake.htm to the *Oxford University Museum of Natural History*'s "Learning Zone" **website** about minerals.

7. How are minerals and cake alike and different?

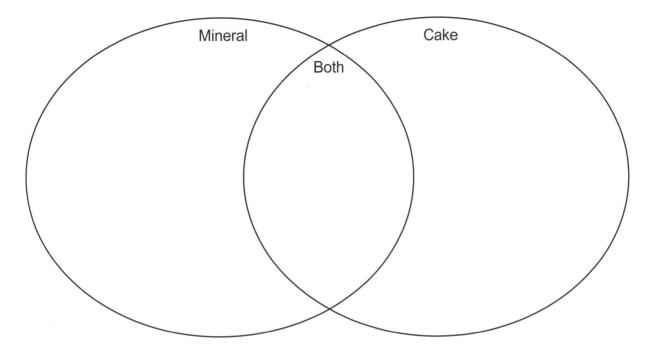

Mineral   Both   Cake

 Click on "What is a mineral? The quiz!"

8. Which of these are minerals? Circle the correct answers.

quartz	granite	gold	amber
charcoal	hematite	plastic	icebergs

Go to http://videos.howstuffworks.com/discovery/34880-howstuffworks-show-episode-6-dangers-of-lead-mining-video.htm to watch the *HowStuffWorks* "Dangers of Lead Mining" **video**.

9. Where are some of the highest concentrations of lead on Earth?

    _____

10. Explain why lead mining can be dangerous.

    _____

    _____

    _____

    _____

Go to http://videos.howstuffworks.com/discovery/30924-modern-gold-mining-video.htm to watch the *HowStuffWorks* "Modern Gold Mining" **video**.

11. What would you do if you lived near a stream rich in tiny gold fragments? Would you become a modern gold miner? Would the expense and hard work be worth the reward? On a separate piece of paper, explain your decision with examples from the video. Use the chart to plan your answer.

Benefits of Gold Mining	Difficulties of Gold Mining

Rocks

 Use the **key words** in each question to find the answers on the Internet.

1. Complete the chart on the three classes of rocks.

Classes of Rocks

Igneous	Sedimentary	Metamorphic
Formed by	Formed by	Formed by
Examples	Examples	Examples
• • • • •	• • • • •	• • • • •

2. Which class of rock contains fossils?

_____

3. Which class of rock makes up the majority of Earth's crust?

_____

4. Marble is a metamorphic rock. What type of rock did it metamorphose from?

_____

5. What are three basic types of rock on the moon?

_____   _____   _____

Go to http://curator.jsc.nasa.gov/lunar/ to read *NASA*'s "Lunar Rocks and Soils from Apollo Missions" **article**.

6. What have scientists learned from studying the moon rocks from the Apollo missions?

_____

_____

_____

7. Why do scientists hope to study samples of rocks from other planets in our solar system?

_____

_____

Go to http://www.oum.ox.ac.uk/thezone/rocks/cycle/index.htm to the *Oxford University Museum of Natural History*'s "The Learning Zone" **website** about the rock cycle.

8. How do rocks change from one type to another? On a separate piece of paper, draw and label the rock cycle diagram to explain. Use the words below to label your diagram.

compaction/ cementation	deposition	erosion	extrusion
igneous	intrusive crystallization	melting	**metamorphic**
metamorphism	**sedimentary**	uplift	weathering

Go to http://www.schooltube.com/video/1db4b49ffe290cd8fd16/Igneous-Rock-Formation to watch *SchoolTube*'s "Igneous Rock Formation" **video**.

9. Take notes from the video using these key words:

molten rock	floats	intrusive igneous rock	plume of volcanic gases
lava tubes	sinks	extrusive igneous rock	

10. **CHALLENGE** Summarize the video. Be sure to describe how new rock is formed from the volcanic eruptions and the difference between intrusive and extrusive igneous rock.

_____

_____

_____

_____

_____

_____

_____

_____

_____

_____

_____

Plate Tectonics

 Use the **key words** in each question to find the answers on the Internet.

1. Define plate tectonics.

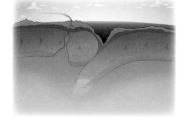

_____

_____

_____

2. 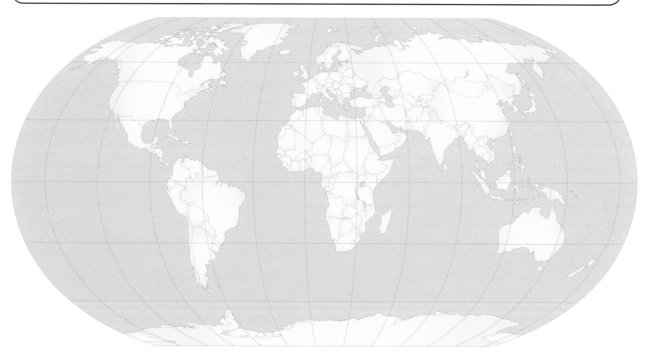 Using the words below, draw and label the tectonic plates (click on **Images** after your key word search).

African	Antarctic	Eurasian	Indo-Australian
Nazca	North American	Pacific	South American

3. Why do earthquakes occur when transform plate boundaries grind past each other?

_____

_____

_____

4. How is new continental crust created in the continental rift zone?

_____

_____

_____

5. **CHALLENGE**   Define subduction. What causes subduction to form mountains and volcanoes?

Subduction

Cause

Effect
Mountains

Cause

Effect
Volcanoes

Go to http://news.discovery.com/earth/videos/why-tell-me-why-why-pangea-broke-apart.htm to watch *Discovery*'s "Why Pangea Broke Apart" **video**.

6. What was Pangaea?

_____

_____

7. Why did Pangaea break apart?

_____

_____

_____

For questions 8-11, go to http://www.teachersdomain.org/asset/ess05_int_shake/ to *A Science Odyssey's* "Mountain Maker, Earth Shaker" **website**.

8. Compare the effects of the three types of boundaries in plate tectonics.

Boundary Name	Convergent	Transform	Divergent
Action of Plates			
Effects of Action			

9. Which action at a transform boundary causes the most rapid change with a burst of movement? Why?

_____

_____

_____

10. Which action at a convergent boundary causes the most gradual or slowest change? Why?

_____

_____

_____

11. If divergent boundary collisions cause continual new growth in the ocean floor, why is Earth not growing larger?

_____

_____

_____

Go to http://science.discovery.com/tv-shows/greatest-discoveries/videos/100-greatest-discoveries-plate-tectonics.htm to watch *Discovery*'s "Plate Tectonics" **video**.

12. List evidence of plate tectonics shown in the video.

Subduction (Convergent)	Strike/Slip (Transform)	Uplifting (Convergent)

13. Choose one example from the above list and explain how it reshapes the geography of Earth. (Describe images from the video to give details to your explanation.)

_____

_____

_____

_____

_____

Earthquakes

 Use the **key words** in each question to find the answers on the Internet.

1. In geology, what is the difference between a plate and a fault?

   _____

   _____

   _____

2. How are the epicenter and hypocenter of an earthquake related?

   _____

   _____

3. How many earthquakes happen (on average) per day on Earth?

   _____

4. Between 1974 and 2003, California experienced 4,895 recorded earthquakes, the second-highest number in the United States. Which state had the most earthquakes? How many more than California?

   _____   _____

5. Southern California has more than 300 faults along the boundary of the Pacific Plate and the North American Plate. Use an image search to locate these four major (and most active) faults and label them on the map below.

San Andreas Fault   San Jacinto Fault   Elsinore Fault   Imperial Fault

For questions 6-8, go to http://video.nationalgeographic.com/video/environment/ environment-natural-disasters/earthquakes/earthquake-101/ to watch *National Geographic*'s "Earthquake 101" **video**.

6. How does an earthquake occur? Describe the movement within Earth before, during, and after an earthquake.

Before	During	After

7. How are seismic waves measured? Describe how seismographs work and how earthquakes are ranked using the Richter scale.

_____

_____

_____

_____

8. Why do engineers and architects study earthquakes?

_____

_____

_____

For questions 9-11, go to http://video.nationalgeographic.com/video/environment/environment-natural-disasters/earthquakes/japan-tsunami-2011-vin/ to watch *National Geographic*'s "Earthquakes: Rare Video: Japan Tsunami" **video**.

9. List important details about the earthquake and tsunami from the video.

Natural Disaster

Date	Location

Size		Size
	Earthquake ← → Tsunami	

Damages	Damages

10. **CHALLENGE** How do earthquakes cause tsunamis?

_____

_____

11. Illustrate the difference between tsunami waves in deep water and shallow water.

Deep Water	Shallow Water

Go to http://www.stopdisastersgame.org/en/playgame.html to the *International Strategy for Disaster Reduction*'s "Stop Disasters!" **game**.

12. While experimenting with ways to prevent destruction, take notes about what is effective and ineffective to save lives and protect property.

Effective Defenses	Ineffective Defenses

13. [CHALLENGE] Analyze your results. How would you design a future city on Japan's coastline? Describe protective measures that were effective in saving lives and protecting property in the event of an earthquake and tsunami.

_____

_____

_____

_____

_____

_____

_____

_____

_____

For questions 14-16, go to http://earthquake.usgs.gov/learn/kids/ to use the *U.S. Geological Survey*'s "Earthquakes for Kids" **website**. Use your critical thinking skills to locate the answers to the following questions using the links on this website.

14. Where was the December 26, 2004, earthquake? What was its magnitude? How many countries were affected by it?

_____

_____

_____

15. List key details about the largest recorded earthquake in the world.

Largest Recorded Earthquake

Location	Date	Magnitude

16. What does a geophysicist do? Write a job description for a geophysicist. (Include responsibilities and work locations.)

_____

_____

_____

_____

_____

_____

_____

Volcanoes

 Use the **key words** in each question to find the answers on the Internet.

1. Define volcano.

   _____

   _____

   _____

2. What is the Ring of Fire?

   _____

   _____

3. What is the difference between lava and magma?

Lava	Magma

4. Where is the most active volcano on Earth? What is its name? Why are people able to get close to this continuously erupting volcano?

Volcano	Location

Why People Can Be Close

Search the Internet for **images** of the different types of volcanoes.

5. Sketch diagrams of the different types of volcanoes. Use the words in each box to label your picture.

Cinder Cone	Composite Volcano
fine ash, magma, vent, cinder	lava, ash, magma, vent, branch pipe

Shield Volcano	Lava Dome
magma, vent, lava flow	magma, vent, lava flow

For questions 6-8, go to http://www.neok12.com/php/watch.php?v=zX06694e581a 074f6e005367&t=Volcanoes to watch the *BBC*'s "How Volcanoes Form" **video**.

6. Illustrate and label the three layers of the inside of Earth.

    From which layer do volcanic eruptions originate? _____

7. **CHALLENGE** How do volcanoes form? Describe the process.

At Constructive Plate Boundaries	At Destructive Plate Boundaries	In the Middle of Plates

8. How did studying the islands of Hawaii help scientists develop the theory of hot spots in Earth's mantle?

    _____

    _____

For questions 9-12, go to http://www.nhm.ac.uk/kids-only/earth-space/volcanoes/
to The Natural History Museum's "Volcanoes" **website**.

9. Click on "Build a volcano." Which combination makes a cinder cone volcano?

	(circle one)
Lava can be	runny or sticky
and can contain	lots of water or little water

10. Click on "Lava." What is viscosity? What makes lava more viscous?

_____

_____

_____

11. Click on "Gases." Name three poisonous gases that explode from volcanoes.

_____   _____   _____

12. Click on "Water." How does the amount of water vapor in lava affect a volcano's
eruption?

_____

_____

_____

13. Use the Internet to research one of these volcanic events. Describe the extent of the destruction on things such as the landscape, wildlife, cities, humans, weather, etc. Use the chart to record your findings before writing your paragraph.

choose one	The AD 79 Eruption of Italy's Mt. Vesuvius (buried the entire city of Pompeii under ash, preserving it for all time)	The 1883 Eruption of Indonesia's Mt. Krakatau (created a blast heard 3,000 miles away that completely broke the volcanic mountain apart)
Effect on Landscape		
Effect on Wildlife		
Effect on Cities		
Effect on Humans		
Effect on Weather		

_____

_____

_____

_____

_____

_____

Section 6

Plants

Plants are living organisms on Earth that produce their own food through the process of photosynthesis. Most plants are immobile due to their root systems and convert light energy into protein through green chlorophyll molecules. The basic structure of a plant is root, stem, and leaves.

The plant kingdom can be divided into two groups: vascular and non-vascular. Vascular plants have a system of tubes to transport water and food. Non-vascular plants, such as mosses and liverworts, rely on a constant source of water for food, which prevents them from growing large. Vascular plants are divided into two main groups: flowering and non-flowering plants.

This section on plants presents critical thinking questions for students to search the Internet for answers.

Websites for whole class instruction:
http://plants.usda.gov/java/

http://www.mbgnet.net/bioplants/

http://www.sciencekids.co.nz/videos/nature.html

http://www.knowplants.org/Know_Plants/Home.html

Plants

 Use the **key words** in each question to find the answers on the Internet.

1. How are plant and animals similar and different?

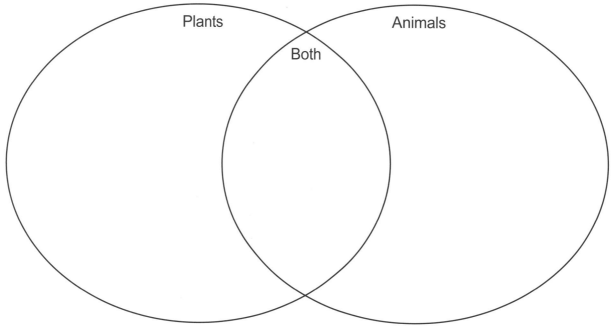

Plants   Animals

Both

2. Name three things plants provide for animals.

_____   _____   _____

3. Define and list examples of angiosperm and gymnosperm plants.

	Angiosperm	Gymnosperm
Definition		
Examples	• • • • •	• • • • •

 For questions 4-8, go to http://urbanext.illinois.edu/gpe/gpe.html to be a detective in *The University of Illinois Extension*'s "The Great Plant Escape" mystery **game**.

4. Use the table to take notes as you solve Case 1.

The Facts of Case 1

Plant Structure	Plant Parts	Life Cycle	Growing Plants Indoors

5. Explain the differences between woody and herbaceous plants.

_____

_____

_____

6. **CHALLENGE** Your flower garden has <u>impatiens</u>, <u>foxgloves</u>, and <u>daisies</u>. On each timeline below, label each flower's life cycle (grow, flower, set seed, and die). Also label each one as annual, perennial, or biennial.

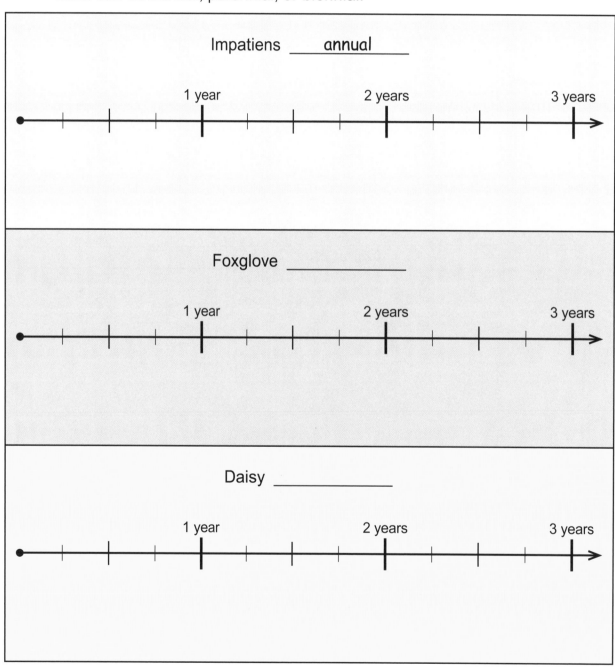

7. How does an indoor plant look when it is not receiving enough light?

_____

_____

8. Sprout ate foods from all different parts of a plant. Name three more foods that people eat from each different part of a plant.

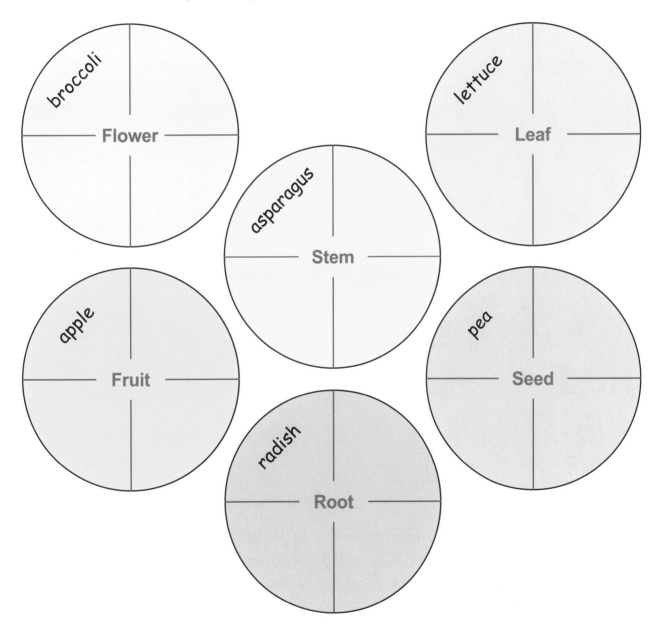

For questions 9-12, go to http://www.ncagr.gov/cyber/kidswrld/plant/nutrient.htm to the *North Carolina Department of Agriculture and Consumer Services*' "Plant Nutrients" **website**.

9. What are the 16 nutrients needed for plant survival?

Non-Mineral Nutrients	Mineral Nutrients	
1.	1.	8.
2.	2.	9.
3.	3.	10.
	4.	11.
	5.	12.
	6.	13.
	7.	

10. How do plants use the non-minerals?

_____

_____

11. Why do farmers and gardeners add fertilizer to soil?

_____

_____

_____

12. **CHALLENGE** Imagine you are a farmer. What kind of soil would you prefer to plant your crop in? Describe the ideal soil texture and soil pH for your plants. How will you ensure your crops get all the nutrients they need from the soil?

_____

_____

_____

_____

Go to http://video.nationalgeographic.com/video/kids/green-kids/plants-kids/ to watch *National Geographic Kids*' "Green: Plants" **video**.

13. Label the circle of plant life in the rain forest described in the video.

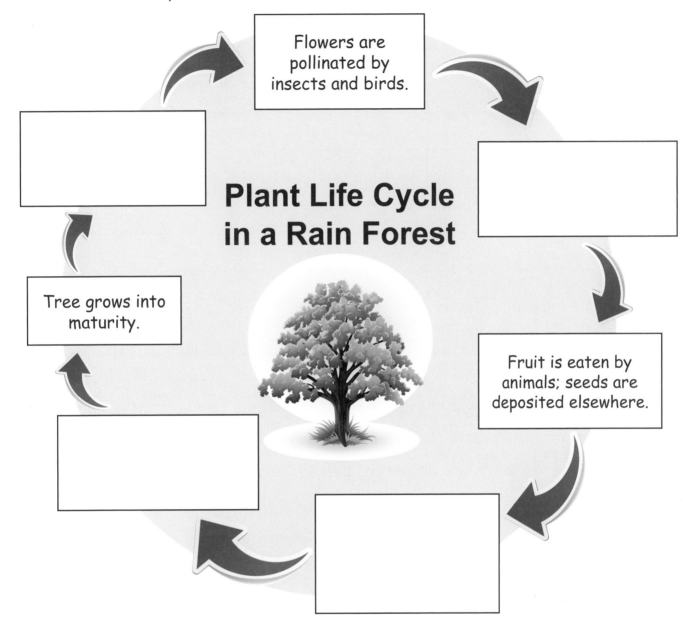

Plant Life Cycle in a Rain Forest

Flowers are pollinated by insects and birds.

Fruit is eaten by animals; seeds are deposited elsewhere.

Tree grows into maturity.

Plant Cells

 Use the **key words** in each question to find the answers on the Internet.

1. What is chlorophyll?

   _____

   _____

   _____

2. What is photosynthesis?

   _____

   _____

3. Where are the plant cells that carry out photosynthesis located?

   _____

 For questions 4-6, go to http://www.sheppardsoftware.com/health/anatomy/cell/ plant_cell_tutorial.htm to *Sheppard Software*'s "Plant Cell" **interactive website**.

4. What are the similarities and differences between an animal cell and a plant cell?

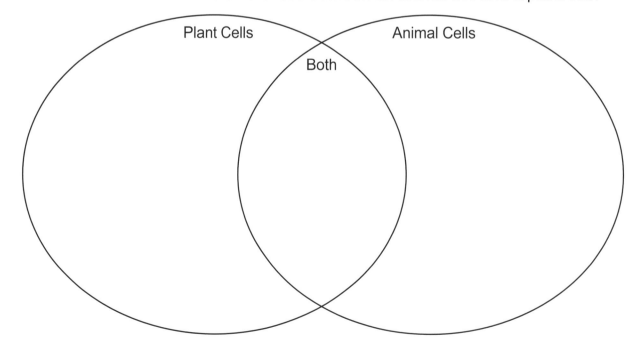

5. What does each cell part do? Describe their functions.

Cell Part	Function
cell wall	surrounds and protects the cell and gives it structure
plasma membrane	
chloroplast	
cytoplasm	
endoplasmic reticulum	
Golgi apparatus	
mitochondria	
nucleus	
ribosome	
vacuole	
peroxisomes	

Now play the "Plant Cell Game."

6. On a separate sheet of paper, sketch the final picture and label the plant cell parts using the words below.

mitochondria	vacuole	cytoplasm	nucleus
cell wall	ribosomes	chloroplast	peroxisomes
plasma membrane	endoplasmic reticulum	Golgi apparatus	

Go to http://www.watchknowlearn.org/Video.aspx?VideoID=20219 to watch *WatchKnowLearn*'s "Parts of a Plant Cell" **video**.

7. There are different types of plant cells for specific plant functions. Complete the table by describing the function of each cell.

Cell Type	Primary Function
Plant Cell Containing Chloroplasts	
Exterior Root Plant Cells Containing Hairs	
Phloem Cells Within the Root	
Xylem Cells Within the Root	

8. **CHALLENGE** Explain how different plant cells work together to feed and nourish the plant.

_____

_____

_____

_____

Go to http://studyjams.scholastic.com/studyjams/jams/science/plants/photosynthesis.htm to watch *Scholastic*'s "Photosynthesis" **video**.

9. Write a recipe for photosynthesis. Include the list of ingredients and complete directions that any green plant may follow to produce its own food.

List of Ingredients
•
•
•
•

Equipment Needed (Plant Parts)
•
•
•
•
•
•

Step by Step Instructions
1.
2.
3.
4.

End Products

Flowering Plants

 Use the **key words** in each question to find the answers on the Internet.

1. What is the approximate number of species of flowering plants?

   _____

2. Name three examples of a blue angiosperm.

   _____   _____   _____

3. How does a flowering plant use seeds to reproduce?

   _____

   _____

4. What are differences between plants that are pollinated by insects versus plants pollinated by wind?

Pollinated by Insects	Pollinated by Wind
• • •	• long stamens and pistils • • •

5. Which flowering plant produces the heaviest seed (40 lbs/17.6 kg!)?

   _____

 Search the Internet for **images** of the parts of a flower.

6. On a separate piece of paper, draw and label the parts of a flower using the words below.

petal	sepal	stem	leaf
pistil	stigma	style	ovary	ovule
stamen	anther	filament	receptacle

7. On a separate piece of paper, describe how the parts of flowers attract pollinators such as birds and insects.

For questions 8-10, go to http://www.mnh.si.edu/museum/news/firstflower/ to the *Smithsonian National Museum of Natural History*'s "Earth's First Flower?" **website**.

8. How old is the flowering plant fossil? Where was it discovered?

_____

_____

9. How can enclosing seeds inside fruit lead to a plant's survival?

_____

_____

_____

10. What does a paleobotanist study?

_____

_____

For questions 11-13, go to http://www.neok12.com/Pollination.htm to watch **videos** about pollination.

Watch "The Beauty of Pollination" **video**.

11. Which animals and insects are featured pollinating flowers?

_____ _____ _____

_____ _____ _____

12. What do some of the flowers become after pollination?

_____

13. Watch "The Life Cycle of a Flowering Plant" **video**. Take notes to describe each of the four stages in the life cycle of a flowering plant.

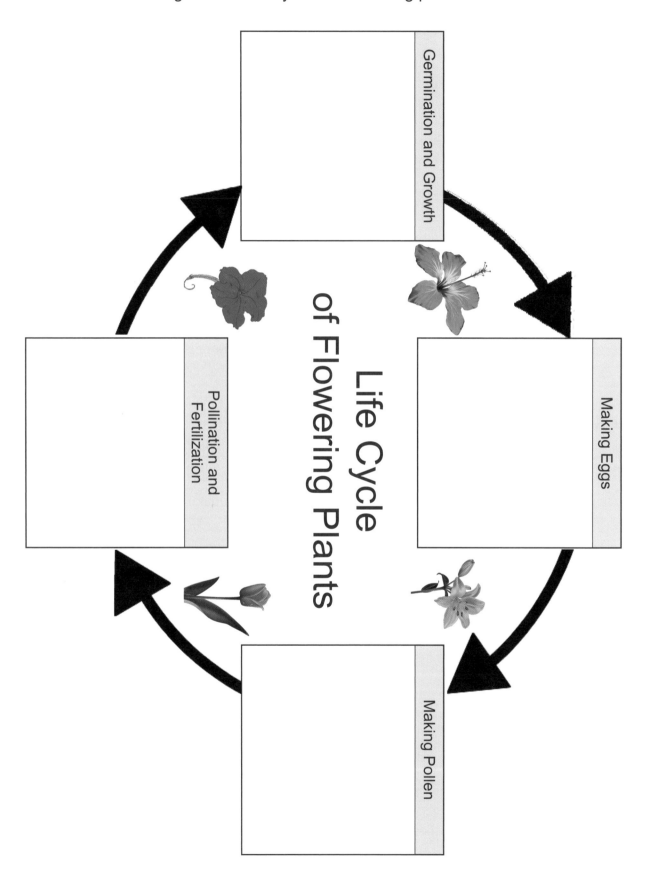

Non-Flowering Plants

 Use the **key words** in each question to find the answers on the Internet.

1. What is a spore?

   _____

   _____

2. Where are spores located on ferns?

   _____

3. Is a mushroom a non-flowering plant? Why or why not?

   _____

   _____

   _____

4. What is a rhizome?

   _____

   _____

5. **CHALLENGE** Explain the difference between a bulb and a tuber.

   _____

   _____

   _____

6. Describe each non-flowering plant.

Non-Flowering Plant	Description
Green Algae	
Mosses	
Ferns	
Worts	
Horsetails	

 For questions 7-8, go to http://www.buzzle.com/articles/non-flowering-plants-list .html to *Buzzle*'s "Non-Flowering Plant List" **website**.

7. Compare and contrast flowering and non-flowering plants.

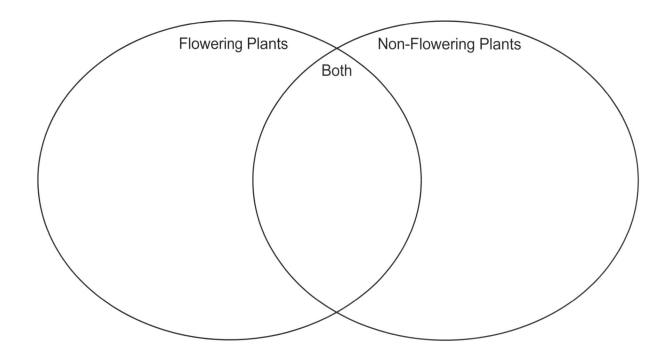

Flowering Plants   Non-Flowering Plants

Both

8. Draw pictures of the non-flowering plants and give the common name for each.

Botanical Name: **Marchantia**	Botanical Name: **Drepanocladus**	Botanical Name: **Grimmia**	Botanical Name: **Sphagnum**
Known as: _____	Known as: _____	Known as: _____	Known as: _____
Botanical Name: **Lygodium**	Botanical Name: **Woodsia**	Botanical Name: **Pteridum**	Botanical Name: **Microsorum Pustulatum**
Known as: _____	Known as: _____	Known as: _____	Known as: _____
Botanical Name: **Spruce**	Botanical Name: **Abies**	Botanical Name: **Ginkgo**	Botanical Name: **Sciadopitys**
Known as: _____	Known as: _____	Known as: _____	Known as: _____

Go to http://www.ehow.com/video_4774756_do-non_flowering-plants-reproduce_ .html to watch *Garden Guides'* "How Do Nonflowering Plants Reproduce?" **video**.

9. Take notes on the different ways non-flowering plants reproduce.

Name of Way Used to Reproduce	Description

10. Explain three ways non-flowering plants reproduce.

_____

_____

_____

_____

_____

_____

_____

_____

Fruits and Vegetables

 Use the **key words** in each question to find the answers on the Internet.

1. What is the main difference between a fruit and a vegetable?

_____

_____

2. Give examples of different types of vegetables.

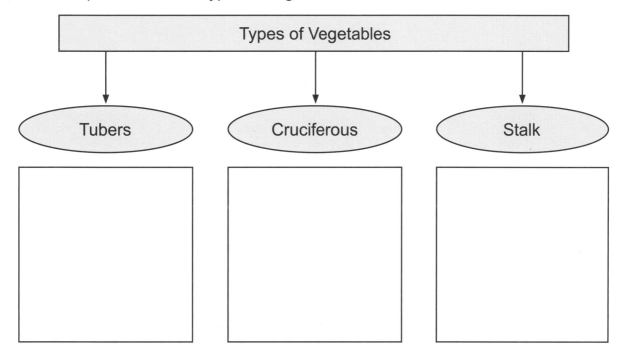

3. Which state produces the most apples?

_____

4. Which nut is the peach related to?

_____

5. How many pounds of tomatoes does the average American eat each year?

_____

6. Sort the following foods into the correct categories.

| corn | artichoke | rice | tomato |
| wheat | bok choy | onion | celery |

Fruits	Vegetables

 Go to http://video.nationalgeographic.com/video/places/countries-places/united-states/us_cranberries/ to watch *National Geographic*'s "United States: Cranberry Harvest" **video**.

7. Explain the process of harvesting cranberries.

_____

_____

_____

_____

_____

8. Describe three uses of water in growing and harvesting cranberries.

_____

_____

_____

Go to http://www.time.com/time/video/player/0,32068,658160623001_2030619,00 .html to watch *TIME*'s "Aquaponics: Using Fish Poop to Grow Vegetables" **video**.

9. What is aquaponics?

_____

10. List two benefits to growing vegetables using aquaponics.

_____

_____

_____

Go to http://www.gardenersworld.com/how-to/projects/basics/how-to-practise-crop- rotation/94.html to watch the *BBC*'s "Gardeners' World" **video** on crop rotation.

11. How does crop rotation help vegetable growth? Draw the vegetables that belong in each garden plot below. Explain their benefit to the soil and the order of rotation.

Go to http://www.unitedstreaming.com/videos/dsc/externalApplications/virtual_labs-es/Plants/index.html to be an agronomist and play *Discovery Education Science*'s "How Does Your Garden Grow" **virtual lab**. Select Level 1.

12. **CHALLENGE** How do the various growing conditions affect the size of the tomatoes?

Trial	Soil	Light	Water	Tomatoes Per Plant	Tomato Size
1	sand	medium	medium	4	small
2					
3					
4					
5					
6					
7					
8					
9					
10					

Trees and Shrubs

 Use the **key words** in each question to find the answers on the Internet.

1. Name three things trees give to Earth and explain the importance of each.

_____

_____

_____

2. What is the largest tree species? _____

3. Describe the differences between angiosperms and gymnosperms.

Angiosperms	Gymnosperms
•	•
•	•
•	•
•	•

4. Sort the following trees into the correct categories.

apple	pine	magnolia	oak
redwood	maple	cedar	spruce

Angiosperms	Gymnosperms

5. Why would someone hire an arborist?

_____

_____

_____

_____

Search the Internet for **images** of the parts of a tree.

6. On a separate piece of paper, draw and label the parts of a tree using the words below. Then, explain the purpose or function of each part.

leaves	branches	trunk	woody roots	roots

For questions 7-9, go to http://www.neok12.com/Plants.htm to watch *NeoK12*'s "Trees" **video**.

7. Which tree part makes trees different from other plants?

_____

_____

8. Why do trees need large, woody trunks?

_____

_____

9. How does a dead tree contribute to a forest ecosystem?

_____

_____

For questions 10-12, go to http://www.arborday.org/trees/wtit/ to the *Arbor Day Foundation*'s "What Tree is That?" website and launch the **animation**.

10. Use the clues to help you identify this mystery tree.

Clue	Description	Result	
1			
2			
3			

11. **CHALLENGE** Use the clues to help you identify this mystery tree.

Clue	Description	
1		
2		
3		
4		
		Result
5		
6		
7		

12. Imagine you are an expert tree identifier. What parts of the tree do you examine to learn the tree's type? On a separate piece of paper, make a list of features to inspect to determine a tree's type.

 Go to http://www.arborday.org/Shopping/Trees/shrubs-bushes-and-hedges.cfm to browse the *Arbor Day Foundation*'s **website** to select the perfect shrubs for your location's climate and weather.

13. Design a yard using a variety of shrubs. Record the name of each shrub purchased and its price. Challenge: Do not spend more than $100.

Name of Shrub	Price		Quantity of Shrubs		Cost for Shrubs
	$	x		=	$
	$	x		=	$
	$	x		=	$
	$	x		=	$
	$	x		=	$
				Total amount spent	$

14. On a separate piece of paper, sketch this yard with the planting arrangement and label your new shrubs.

Section 7

Space

Our Solar System and Beyond

Astronomy is the study of the universe, which includes the stars, planets, moons, and trillions of other objects it contains. Because the universe is all matter and energy that exists anywhere and everywhere, studying the universe is truly the study of all things. This section limits its explorations to the relatively small objects in our galaxy, The Milky Way.

This section on space presents critical thinking questions for students to search the Internet for answers.

Websites for whole class instruction:
http://www.space.com

http://www.nasa.gov/mission_pages/station/main/index.html

http://www.planetary.org

http://teachspacescience.org/cgi-bin/ssrtop.plex

http://ncesse.org

http://starchild.gsfc.nasa.gov/docs/StarChild/StarChild.html

Our Solar System

 Use the **key words** in each question to find the answers on the Internet.

1. List the eight planets in our solar system beginning with the one closest to the sun and ending with the one farthest from the sun.

   _____

   _____

   _____

2. How do scientists define a planet?

   a. _____

   _____

   b. _____

   _____

   c. _____

   _____

3. Why was Pluto demoted to a dwarf planet?

   _____

   _____

   _____

   _____

   _____

For questions 4-13, go to http://video.nationalgeographic.com/video/science/ space-sci/solar-system/solar-system-sci/ to view *National Geographic*'s "Solar System 101" **video**.

4. What accounts for 99% of the solar system's mass and binds our solar system together?

   _____

5. What is the extreme temperature range of Mercury?

   _____

6. Which planet is considered Earth's nearest twin? _____

   In what three ways is it similar to Earth?

   _____   _____   _____

7. What covers 70% of Earth's surface?

   _____

8. Name three geographical features of Mars.

   _____

9. What is Jupiter's great red spot?

   _____

10. What makes up Saturn's rings?

   _____

11. What is Uranus's most unique feature?

   _____

12. Which is considered the windiest planet? _____

13. At its greatest distance, how far is the dwarf planet Pluto from the sun?

   _____

Go to http://video.nationalgeographic.com/video/science/space-sci/solar-system/
transit-venus-sci/ to watch *National Geographic*'s "Solar System: The Transit of
Venus and Kepler Mission" **video**.

14. What is the transit of Venus and when will the next one occur?

_____

_____

Go to http://video.nationalgeographic.com/video/news/space-technology-news/
mars-curiosity-rover-lands-vin/ to watch *National Geographic*'s "Space & Tech
News: Mars Curiosity Rover Landing a Success—NASA Jubilant" **video**.

15. What is the purpose of the Mars Rover Curiosity mission?

_____

_____

Go to http://video.nationalgeographic.com/video/news/space-technology-news/
nasa-juno-spacecraft-vin/ to watch *National Geographic*'s "Space & Tech News:
NASA Probe to Explore Jupiter" **video**.

16. How does Earth's gravity help propel the Juno spacecraft?

_____

_____

Go to http://spaceplace.nasa.gov/solar-system-explorer/ to play *NASA*'s "Explore
the Solar System" **game**. While you explore Saturn, click "Play Game" to play
"The Cassini Commander."

17. Why is your spaceship drawn toward a moon as it passes?

_____

_____

18. Compare and contrast the largest and smallest planets of our solar system's eight planets.

Features	Largest Planet Jupiter	Smallest Planet Mercury
Mass		
Diameter		
Temperature		
Distance From the Sun		
Length of Day and Year		

19. Imagine you live on the largest planet and you are writing a letter to your cousin on the smallest planet. Describe a day on your planet. What is the weather like? How is your planet like your cousin's? How do you spend your time during the day (remember how long a day is on your planet)?

Dear _____,

_____

_____

_____

_____

_____

_____

_____

_____

Your cousin,

_____

The Sun

 Use the **key words** in each question to find the answers on the Internet.

1. Which gases make up 98% of the sun?

    _____   _____

2. Define heliocentric.

helio		centric		Definition
meaning	+		=	

3. Name four things the sun provides for us to live on Earth.

    _____   _____

    _____   _____

4. Draw the layers of the sun and label them using the words below.

inner core	photosphere	chromosphere	corona
radiative zone	convection zone	subsurface flows	

5. Which layer of Earth's atmosphere protects us the most from the sun's harmful ultraviolet rays?

    _____

For questions 6-10, go to http://video.nationalgeographic.com/video/science/ space-sci/solar-system/sun-101-sci/ to watch *National Geographic*'s "Solar System: Sun 101" **video**.

6. What is fusion?

_____

_____

7. How does Earth benefit from the sun's fusion?

_____

_____

8. Why does Earth stay in orbit around the sun (instead of flying off into outer space)?

_____

_____

9. Complete this cause and effect sequence about how the sun provides for plants which provide for animals.

The sun's light gives energy to plants.	Plants _____ _____ _____ _____	Animals _____ _____ _____

10. Color a picture of the Auroras.

For questions 11-14, go to http://missionscience.nasa.gov/sun/sunVideo_01space weather.html to watch *NASA*'s "Mysteries of the Sun: Space Weather" **video**.

11. What does the sun emit into space?

_____

12. What are two types of storms on the sun?

_____

_____

_____

13. How do geomagnetic storms affect Earth?

_____

_____

_____

14. Why is forecasting space weather important? On a separate piece of paper, describe some of the ways that space weather may disrupt human life.

 Go to http://www.kidsgeo.com/geography-for-kids/0019-the-revolution-of-the-earth.php to *The KidsKnowIt Network*'s "The Revolution of the Earth Around Our Sun" **website**.

15. **CHALLENGE** On a separate piece of paper, draw Earth's seasons at four points in its orbit. Label each hemisphere's winter and summer solstices and each hemisphere's vernal (spring) and autumnal equinoxes.

The Moon

 Use the **key words** in each question to find the answers on the Internet.

1. What is a lunar eclipse?

_____

_____

_____

2. What is the diameter of the moon?

_____

3. What is the distance of the moon from Earth?

_____

4. What is the moon's rotation period (the time it takes for the moon to spin one revolution on its axis)?

_____

5. What is the moon's orbital period (the time it takes the moon to orbit one revolution around Earth)?

_____

6. What is the moon's crust primarily made of?

_____

7. Go to http://www.neok12.com/Moon.htm to watch two of the *neoK12* **videos** about the moon and take notes about facts and details.

Title of 1st Video
Interesting Information

Title of 2nd Video
Interesting Information

 For questions 8-12, go to http://airandspace.si.edu/explore-and-learn/topics/apollo/index.htm to the *Smithsonian*'s "The Apollo Program" **website**.

8. What happened during the Apollo 1 mission?

_____

_____

9. Which six missions landed on the moon and when did each land?

Moon Landings

Mission	Date

10. Why didn't Apollo 13 land on the moon?

_____

_____

Click on "Top 10 Apollo Results" on the *Smithsonian* **website**.

11. Has there ever been life on the moon? Why?

_____

_____

_____

_____

12. Why do scientists continue to study the lunar samples retrieved by the Apollo program?

_____

_____

_____

For questions 13-17, go to http://www.wonderville.ca/asset/phases-of-the-moon to *Wonderville*'s "Phases of the Moon" **interactive website**.

13. Why does the moon appear to shine?

_____

_____

14. Why does a new moon appear dark?

_____

_____

15. Why do we only see one side of the moon?

_____

_____

16. Explain the difference between a waxing moon and a waning moon.

_____

_____

17. Draw and label the phases of the moon.

18. The moon has inspired the work of scientists, astronomers, and even POETS! Be creative and write an original poem about the moon on a separate piece of paper.

Constellations and Stars

 Use the **key words** in each question to find the answers on the Internet.

1. What is a constellation?

   _____

   _____

2. What is the common name of Ursa Major? _____

   Which "smaller" constellation does it contain? _____

3. What is a black hole?

   _____

   _____

4. Name the five circumpolar constellations.

   _____   _____   _____

   _____   _____

5. **CHALLENGE** Many constellations have myths or stories that try to explain their placement in the sky. Research the story of the constellation Orion the Hunter. Use the space provided to take notes.

Who	When	Where

What

Why

6. [CHALLENGE] Write a summary of his story explaining who Orion was and how he became a constellation of stars in the winter sky.

_____

_____

_____

_____

_____

_____

_____

_____

7. On a separate piece of paper, draw and label a picture of the constellation Orion and his imaginary figure.

For questions 8-13, go to http://www.bbc.co.uk/schools/gcsebitesize/science/add_aqa/stars/lifecyclestarsrev1.shtml to *BBC*'s "Life Cycles of Stars" **website**.

8. What attracts dust and gas together to form stars? (page 1)

_____

_____

9. Why is a star stable during its main sequence period? (page 1)

_____

_____

10. Draw, color, and label each star in the life cycle flowchart. (page 2)

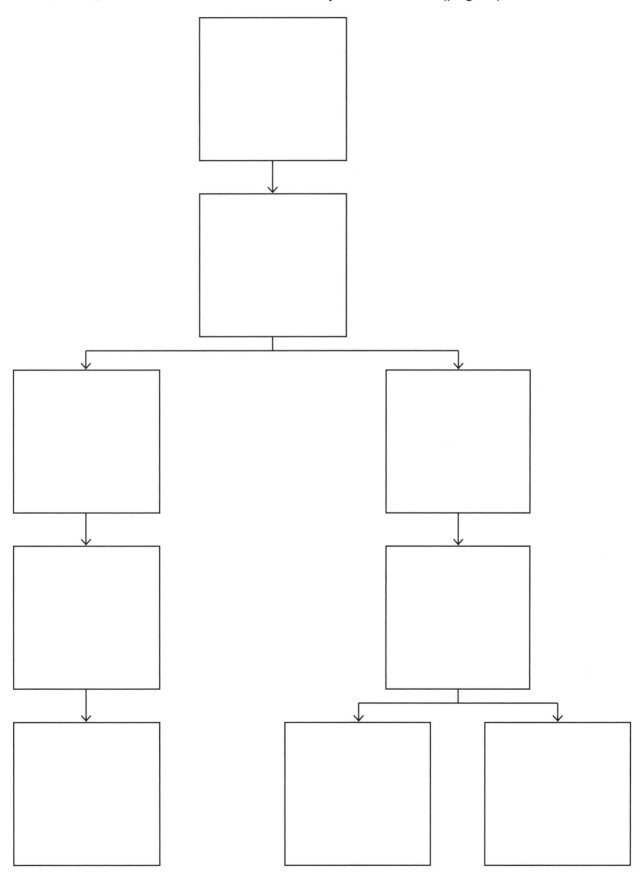

11. How does the size of a star affect its life cycle? (page 2)

_____

_____

12. Explain what occurs when nuclear fusion takes place. (page 3)

_____

_____

13. What are the two main elements involved in a star's nuclear fusion? (page 3)

_____

Go to http://www.bbc.co.uk/schools/gcsebitesize/science/add_aqa/stars/planetsstars andgalaxiesact.shtml to watch *BBC*'s "Life Cycles of Stars – Stars Activity" **video**.

14. How old is our star — the sun? What stage is the sun in its life cycle?

_____

For questions 15-21, go to http://www.neok12.com/Stars.htm to watch the *neoK12* **videos**. First, for questions 15-18, watch "The Beauty of Stars Being Born."

15. What is a star-forming nebula?

_____

16. Why do scientists think proplets may one day form planets and not stars?

_____

_____

17. How does the brightest star in the Orion Nebula affect nearby discs?

_____

_____

18. Explain the cause of interesting shapes within the Orion Nebula.

_____

_____

> For questions 19-21, stay on the *neoK12* website and watch NASA's "Seeing Stars" **video**.

19. Describe the star Betelgeuse.

Type	Age	Size	Color

20. What do the colors blue, red and yellow indicate in stars?

_____

_____

21. Describe the conditions required in the habitable zone around a star.

_____

_____

Space Exploration

 Use the **key words** in each question to find the answers on the Internet.

1. Define astronomer.

   _____

   _____

2. Define astronomical unit.

   _____

3. What distance is equal to one light year?

   _____ miles

4. How long is a parsec and what do astronomers measure in parsecs?

   _____

5. Complete the table for three of the seven famous astronomers below.

Astronomers You Should Know

Astronomer	Dates (birth-death)	Country of Birth	Notable Contribution
Nicolaus Copernicus			
Galileo Galilei			
Sir Isaac Newton			
Stephen Hawking			
Edmund Halley			
Edwin Hubble			
Carl Sagan			

6. When did each of these milestone events occur? Which countries and astronauts were involved?

Cold War Space Race

Milestone	Date	Country	Astronauts
1st Satellite in Orbit			
1st Man in Space			
1st American in Orbit			
1st Woman in Space			
1st Moon Landing			
1st Space Lab			
1st Shuttle Mission			

7. CHALLENGE Based on the data in question 6, evaluate which country won the space race and why. Support your answer with evidence from the data.

_____

_____

_____

_____

For questions 8-10, go to http://solc.gsfc.nasa.gov/kids3/kids3.html to watch *NASA*'s "International Space Station (ISS)" **videos**.

8. What is the main purpose of the ISS?

    _____

    _____

9. How many countries participate in the ISS?

    _____

10. Describe a day in the life of an astronaut while living on the ISS.

    _____

    _____

    _____

    _____

    _____

    _____

    _____

    _____

    _____

For questions 11-12, go to http://spaceplace.nasa.gov/mars-adventure2/ to *NASA*'s "Did You Go on a Mars Adventure Yet?" **website**.

11. What are two signs that show Mars once had a water supply?

    _____

    _____

12. Why is NASA exploring Mars?

_____

_____

_____

13. If you could explore any area in space, where would you go? How would you get there? What do you imagine you might find there? On a separate piece of paper, write a creative adventure story about your travels to explore a region in space. Add illustrations when you are finished writing.

Use the chart to plan your story.

Space Adventure

Who	When

Where	How

Conflicts

Discoveries

Asteroids, Meteors, and Comets

Use the **key words** in each question to find the answers on the Internet.

1. Compare and contrast the three terms below.

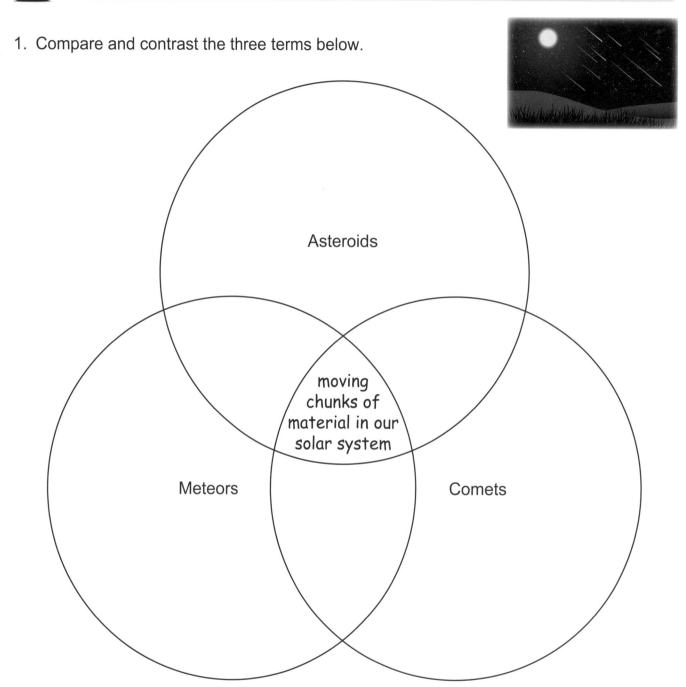

Asteroids

moving chunks of material in our solar system

Meteors

Comets

2. Describe the largest known asteroid in our solar system.

Name	Width	Location	Contents
Ceres			

3. Why do most meteoroids never reach Earth?

_____

_____

_____

4. What is a binary asteroid?

_____

_____

5. How is Pluto like a comet?

_____

_____

Go to http://science.discovery.com/video-topics/space-videos/asteroids.htm to watch *Science Discovery*'s "Asteroid Belt" **video**.

6. Where is the main asteroid belt located?

_____

7. Describe the impact of comet Shoemaker Levy-9 hitting Jupiter.

_____

_____

_____

Go to http://science.nasa.gov/science-news/science-at-nasa/2013/26feb_russian meteor/ to *NASA*'s "What Exploded over Russia?" **news site**.

8. Why do NASA scientists believe the meteor did not come from the DA14 asteroid?

_____

_____

_____

_____

 Go to http://hubblesite.org/reference_desk/faq/answer.php.id=22&cat=solarsystem to *HubbleSite*'s "Frequently Asked Questions" **website**.

9. What is the difference between a meteor, meteoroid, and meteorite?

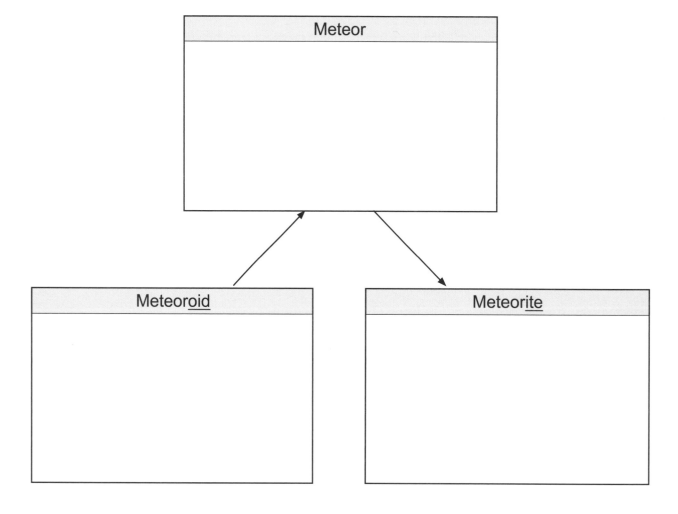

For questions 10-13, go to http://www.tlc.com/tv-shows/other-shows/videos/solar-empire-shorts-origin-of-comets.htm to watch *The Learning Channel*'s "Origin of Comets" **video**.

10. What is the Oort Cloud?

_____

_____

11. What does a comet look like?

_____

_____

12. What are the ingredients for replicating comets?

_____   _____

_____   _____

13. How are comets pushed out of the Oort Cloud?

_____

_____

 Go to http://science.howstuffworks.com/29277-100-greatest-discoveries-halleys-comet-video.htm to watch *HowStuffWorks*' "100 Greatest Discoveries: Halley's Comet" **video**.

14. Why was the discovery of Halley's Comet significant?

_____

_____

_____

_____

15. Pretend an asteroid, meteoroid, or comet is on a collision course with Earth and you are the only scientist who can stop it. On a separate piece of paper, write a story about the possible event and describe your actions to stop the asteroid's impact with Earth. Use the chart to plan key elements of your story.

Setting

Conflicts	Solutions

Final Outcome

Answers

Section 1 – Animals

Amphibians pp. 2-4

1. Coldblooded or ectothermic animals regulate their body temperatures by their surroundings and must hibernate during winter in cold climate habitats, but are active year-round in the tropical/warmer habitats.

2. Metamorphosis is a major change in physical structure that some animals undergo as they become adults.

3.

Group 1	Group 2	Group 3
salamanders, newts, and mudpuppies	caecilians	frogs and toads

tails	no legs	four legs
slender bodies	short tails	no tails
four legs		

4. Chinese giant salamander; 6 feet long; 140 lbs

5. Poison-producing glands in their skin would secrete and poison on touch.

6. The painted chubby frog colors mimic the tree bark and forest floor with brown and tan stripes. The axolotl salamander adapts by regenerating lost body parts and uses gills and lungs for breathing. Answers for new amphibian will vary.

7. Answers will vary.

8. Sample answer:

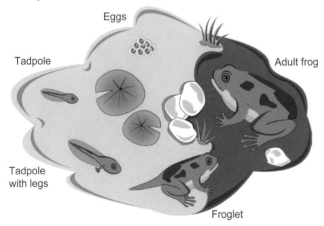

9. Sample answers for Venn diagram:

Water-Holding Frog	Both	Human
• absorbs and holds enough water for two years in its skin • goes into self-induced coma for two years to endure the wait for water	• need water to survive	• can only survive for about three days without water • cannot go into a coma to wait for water

10. The frog absorbs and holds enough water for two years in its skin; humans can only survive for approximately three days without water so they must carry a supply of water. The frog can go into a self-induced coma to endure the two-year wait for water; humans cannot. Humans can survive approximately three weeks without food.

11. Humans dissect animals to learn about animal anatomy. Frogs have a similar internal anatomy structure to humans.

Animal Cells   pp. 5-7

1. nucleus

2. everything enters and exits through both

3. mitochondria

4. ribosome

5. two identical daughter cells

6. Sample answer:

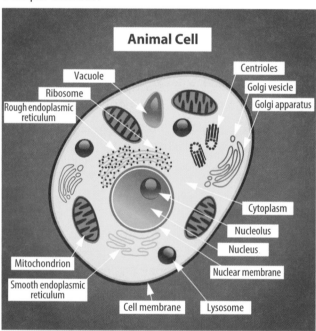

7.

Phase Name of Mitosis	Summary of Events Occurring
1. Interphase	Longest phase; appears inactive, but DNA replicating, centrioles dividing and proteins produced.
2. Prophase	Nucleolus fades and chromatin condenses into chromosomes; microtubules disassemble.
3. Prometaphase	Nucleus breaks down, spindle fibers elongate and attach to chromosomes or overlap each other at cell center.
4. Metaphase	All chromosomes align in one plane at center of cell.
5. Anaphase	Spindle fibers shorten and chromatids pull apart and move to cell poles.
6. Telophase	Chromatids arrive at cell poles.
7. Cytokinesis	Contractile rings cleave the cell into two daughter cells; microtubules reorganize for the return to interphase.

8. Paragraph should reflect above phases from the cell's point of view expressing how it feels to elongate and divide in two.

9. (in this order) rhinovirus, Ebola virus, staphylococcus, e. coli, baker's yeast

10. approx. 20 minutes

11. respiratory difficulty, chest pain, fever and malaise; rapid

Birds   pp. 8-11

1. ornithology

2. approx. 218 pounds heavier

3. A campaign to stop hunters from killing the snowy egrets for feathers for trimming ladies' hats in 1886 eventually led to the founding of the Audubon Society in 1905.

4. Sample answer:

Pros of Birds	Cons of Birds
pollination	dirty in cities
food	overpopulation
eat insects and rodents	carry diseases

5. Sample answer:
The pros far outweigh the cons due to the importance of birds supplying food, pollination, and controlling insect populations.

6. Sample answer:

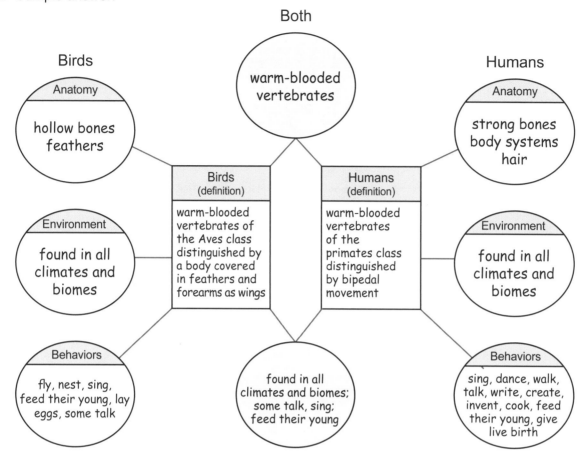

7.

Bird Species	Length of Migration (One Way)	Beginning and Ending Locations of Migration
North American Blue Grouse	approx. 1,000 ft or 300 m	lower to higher altitudes in Rocky Mountains
Rufous Hummingbird	approx. 3,000 miles or 5,000 km	Alaska to Mexico
Arctic Tern	approx. 22,000 miles or 35,500 km	Arctic to Antarctic

8. Answers will vary. Pictures will vary.

9. Questions narrow the type of bird based on color, size, feather patterns, beak style, feet, and leg length.

10. Answers will vary. Stories should include type of bird; descriptions of hazards such as airplanes, clouds, thunderstorms, humans, pesticides, and toxic substances; good sources of energy such as fresh water, berries, worms, etc.; health risks such as pesticides, acid rain, oil spills, etc.

Fish   pp. 12-14

1.

On Earth Today

Largest Mammal		Largest Fish			
blue whale		whale shark			

Weight in Tons		Weight in Tons		Difference	
150 (est.)	–	20.6	=	129.4 tons	

2. (Accept any four): backbone (vertebrate), breathe through gills, cold-blooded, swim in water with fins, lateral line system, sexual reproduction

3. USA 53; Florida 26

4. The world's deadliest fish is the stonefish because it is highly poisonous and hard to see.

5. The coelacanth was thought to have been extinct since the Cretaceous Period over 65 million years ago. Live coelacanths were caught by fishermen in 1938 and 1952 and many have been sighted more recently.

6. Answers will vary.

7. 1. eye   2. eggs   3. liver   4. stomach

    5. intestines   6. heart   7. swim bladder   8. kidney

8. Sample answer:

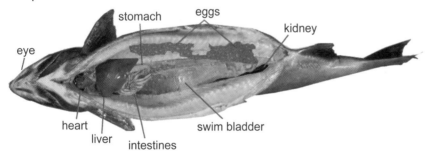

9. swim bladder; additional possible answer: eggs

10. Answers will vary.

11. Sample answer:

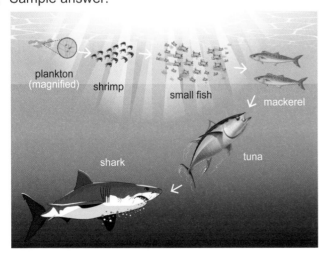

Insects   pp. 15-18

1. entomology

2. Possible answers:

Monarch Butterfly Metamorphosis

Stage 1	Stage 2	Stage 3	Stage 4
egg	larva	pupil	adult
Details: • laid on host plant • many shapes and colors • thin shell that larva eats when it hatches	Details: • caterpillar • lasts 2-4 weeks • eats host plant • grows a lot	Details: • encased in chrysalis • lasts a few days to many months • chrysalis turns clear before hatching	Details: • emerges fully grown from chrysalis • primary purpose is to mate and reproduce • only eats liquid food through proboscis

3. Paragraph should include information from one column of the chart.

4. giant weta, New Zealand; or larval stage Goliath beetle, Africa

5. Exoskeletons prevent growth by only allowing gradual increases in size because the insect must molt periodically, which leaves it vulnerable to predators.

6.

Insect	Effect on Environment	Helpful?	Harmful?
Japanese Beetle	destroys plants by eating the leaves	no	yes
Hornworm Caterpillar	devours a tomato before it ripens	no	yes
Honeybee	pollinates flowers and plants	yes	no

7. Pictures should show a head, thorax, and abdomen.

8. (In any order) compound eyes, antennae, segmented body, six legs, wings, exoskeleton, mouth
   Pictures will vary; all should include these seven features.

9-10. Field trip plan answers will vary.

Invertebrates   pp. 19-20

1. Invertebrates do not have backbones. Vertebrates do have backbones.

2. Heterotrophs are animals that cannot make their own food but rely on other sources for nutrition. Plants are not heterotrophic.

3. sponges

4. Possible answers:

Examples of Echinoderms (any 4)	
starfish	sea urchins
sand dollars	sea cucumbers
sea lilies	feather stars
sea daisies	

Examples of Arthropods (any 4)	
lobster	crab
spider	scorpion
caterpillar	any insect
any arachnid	any crustacean

Characteristics Shared by Echinoderms
• radial symmetry • hard, internal calcite skeleton • all live in salt water/are marine animals

Characteristics Shared by Arthropods
• bilateral symmetry • exoskeleton • live on land and/or under water • segmented bodies • jointed appendages • open circulatory system • compound eyes

5. Answers in paragraph will vary. Comparison should be a synthesis of question 4.

6.

Invertebrates	Phylum
roundworm, ~~scorpion~~, pinworm, hookworm	nematode
squid, ~~crab~~, clam, mussel, oyster	mollusca
spider, shrimp, lobster, centipede, ~~slug~~	arthropoda
~~scallop~~, sea lily, sea urchin, holothurian	echinodermata

7. 97%

8. roundworms or nematodes

9. Sample answer:

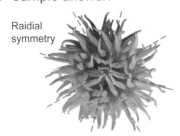
Raidial symmetry

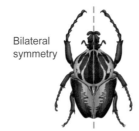
Bilateral symmetry

10. Answers should explain symmetry radiating from a center point and symmetry on either side of a midline.

Mammals   pp. 21-23

1. Answers should include three of the following: produce milk for their young; have hair; neocortex region of the brain; three middle ear bones; lower jaw is a single bone on either side; hearts have an aortic arch; have a diaphragm

2. Monotremes are mammals that lay eggs; examples: platypus and echidna.

3. Marsupials are mammals that are born live but finish development in a pouch on their mother's bellies; examples: kangaroo, koala, wombat, Tasmanian devil, opossum, wallaby, sugar glider.

4.

Animals	Family
melon-headed whale, Orca, dolphin, ~~porpoise~~	Delphinidae
sugar glider, striped possum, ~~flying squirrel~~, wrist-winged glider, great-tailed triok	Petauridae
~~lemming~~, lion, puma, panther, ocelot	Felidae
dingo, jackal, ~~mongoose~~, wolf, Pomeranian	Canidae

5.

Animal	Estimate	Actual Weight	Difference
Blue Whale	Estimates will vary.	200,000-300,000 lbs	Check for correct math to find difference.
Camel		700-2,000 lbs	
Raccoon		10-20 lbs	

6. Answers will vary.

7. Answers will vary.

8. Pictures will vary.

9. Answers will vary.

10. Answers will vary.

Reptiles   pp. 24-27

1. Possible answers: cold-blooded, scales or plates on skin, amniotic eggs, breathe air with lungs, ear holes, vertebrates

2. The inland taipan snake is one of the most venomous snakes in the world.

3. Possible answers: Solomon Island skink, blue-tongue skink, shinglebacked skink, Jackson's chameleon, boas, vipers, garter snakes, Australasian gecko (yellow-bellied three-toed skink), casque-headed lizards, night lizards, plated lizards, sea snakes

4. Sample answers for Venn diagram:

Alligators	Both	Crocodiles
• live in fresh water only • wider, U-shaped snout • only show top teeth when mouth closed • have dermal pressure receptors located on jaw • blackish/grey color • less aggressive • found in southern U.S. and China • average adult size is 4.3 meters	• vertebrates • cold-blooded • lay eggs • can swim about 20 mph • can run about 11 mph • can hold their breath for about an hour • eyes on top of their heads • carnivorous hunters • strong eyesight • sensitive hearing	• can live in salt or fresh water • longer, V-shaped snout • show top and bottom teeth when mouth closed • have dermal pressure receptors located over entire body • olive green/brown color • more aggressive • found in Africa, Australia, and Americas

5. Poison is absorbed or ingested; venom is always injected. Deadly snakes inject their venom when they pierce a body with their fangs. Therefore, they are venomous, not poisonous.

6. The tuatara breed so slowly that rats and humans killed them all.

7. Answers will vary.

8.

Effects on Tuataras

Cause

| Warmer Climate |

→

| Warmer soil would cause the eggs to hatch into males. |

↓

| If all the egg hatchlings are male, they cannot breed. |

↓

| If there are no females for breeding, the tuataras will become extinct. |

9. The purpose of the experiment is to remove one anole species from the environment to see if its species affects another anole species and how their competition affects the environment. The scientist wants to learn about the ecology, behavior, and evolution of the anoles species in southern Florida.

10. body size, growth rate, territory size, habitat use

11. These factors will tell him specifically how they anoles are competing. He will be able to see which species is dominant.

12. Answers will vary but should name a reptile and reasonable answers for each step in the scientific method to create an experiment to conduct with that reptile.

Section 2 – Atmosphere

Climate   pp. 29-32

1. Weather is a specific event or condition that occurs over a period of hours or days. Climate is the average weather in an area over many years.

2. (summit) arctic, high desert, heath/moorland, rain forest, bushland/grazing land (base)

3. Higher elevations have lower temperatures; every 1,000 feet rise in elevation equals -4 degrees Fahrenheit.

4. The Amazon rain forest is located in the equatorial area of South America, mainly Brazil and Peru.

5. The equator receives more direct sunrays, which makes it warmer. The poles receive sunlight at a slight angle making them cooler.

6. Possible answers:

Area	Climate	Possible Weather
North Africa	Mostly dry and hot; Temperature range 32°-130°F	sandstorms; sunny
Central America	Tropical humid; Temperature range 50°-100°F	Heavy rains from September to February; sunny
Europe	Mostly mild climate due to Atlantic Gulf Stream; Temperature range 10°-90°F	rain/sunny

7. Possible answers:
   - Sign: Hotter temperatures; Impact: Too hot for crops to grow or longer growing season
   - Sign: More droughts; Impact: Plants die from lack of irrigation
   - Sign: More severe weather; Impact: Flooding, damaged homes, deaths

8. (In any order):
   - Changing rain and snow patterns
   - Stronger storms
   - Damaged corals
   - Rising sea levels
   - Warmer oceans
   - Changes in plant life cycles
   - Thawing permafrost
   - Less snow and ice
   - More drought and wildfires
   - Higher temperatures and more heat waves
   - Changes in animal migration and life cycles

9. Answers will vary but should be reflective of the chart in question 8.

10. Essays will vary. See rubric for grading:

Score	Content	Organization	Development	Language
4	Answer is appropriate to the question. Content is factually correct.	Clear sense of order. Begins with a thesis or topic sentence.	Supporting points are presented in a logical progression. Develops each point with specific details. Answers question completely.	Uses technical or scientific terminology appropriately and correctly. No major grammatical or spelling errors.
3	Answer is appropriate to the question. Content may have one or two factual errors.	May lack a thesis sentence, but points are presented in a logical progression.	Each point supported with some details and evidence.	Accurate word choice. No more than 2 major errors and a few minor errors.
2	Content relates to the question; contains significant factual errors.	Logic of argument is perceivable. Points presented in a random fashion, but support argument.	Sparse details. Question only partially answered.	Ordinary word choice; use of scientific terminology avoided. Some serious errors.
1	Content not on topic.	Lacks organizational plan.	Statements unrelated to topic.	Limited vocabulary; writing difficult to understand.

Clouds   pp. 33-36

1.

Latin Root	Translation	Describes
cumulo cumulus	"heap"	shape
strato stratus	"layer"	shape
cirro cirrus	"lock of hair" and "high"	shape and height
alto	"medium"	height
nimbus	"rain"	precipitation

2. nimbostratus (or stratonimbus)

3. cirrus

4. Answers will vary. Sample answer:

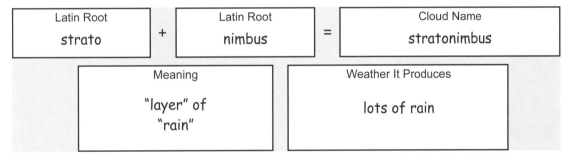

Latin Root		Latin Root		Cloud Name
strato	+	nimbus	=	stratonimbus

Meaning	Weather It Produces
"layer" of "rain"	lots of rain

5. Sample answer: Small clouds contain fewer water droplets, so light can go through them more easily and the cloud can reflect all the colors of the sun, which makes a white appearance. Large clouds contain more water droplets and dust particles, so light cannot penetrate the cloud as easily; the water and dust refract the light making the cloud appear gray rather than white.

6. Cumulonimbus clouds produce thunderstorms containing lightning, hail, heavy rain, and tornadoes.

7.

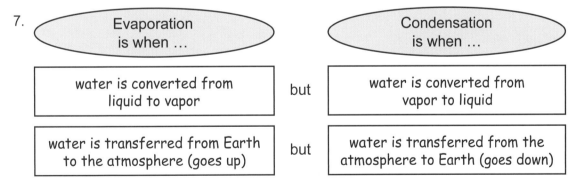

Evaporation is when …		Condensation is when …
water is converted from liquid to vapor	but	water is converted from vapor to liquid
water is transferred from Earth to the atmosphere (goes up)	but	water is transferred from the atmosphere to Earth (goes down)

8. On a hot day at the beach, the process of evaporation is sped up by the heat so more water molecules convert to vapor and enter the atmosphere. As more water enters the atmosphere, the air temperature cools rapidly, causing the water molecules to condense to form tiny liquid droplets, thus forming short rainstorms.

9. moisture, cooling air, condensation nuclei

10-11. Answers will vary. Examples: fog causes transportation accidents; cumulonimbus clouds cause damaging storms with hail, lightning, tornadoes, and thunder; clouds contain lightning.

12. Sample answers*:

Precipitation   pp. 37-41

1. rain, snow, sleet, hail

2. Precipitation falls in liquid form in warmer temperatures.

3. 53.3 inches

4. Sample answers for Venn diagram:

Freezing Rain	Both	Sleet
• surface temp at or below freezing • snow melts and falls as rain • freezes after it is on the ground	• created by melted snow near the edges of warm or cold fronts • begin as snow	• occurs when warm front changes to cold front • snow turns to ice before it hits the ground

* Cloud pictures © 2013 University Corporation for Atmospheric Research

5.

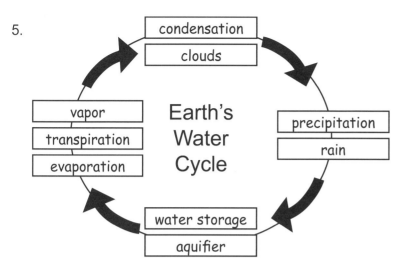

6.

Model	Nature
container	land area; water table
straw	well
white sand	bottom layer of the ground (absorbs water)
modeling clay	confining layer (does not absorb water)
small rocks	hills and valleys (filter water)
green felt	lawn or crop field
cocoa	chemicals and fertilizers
spray bottle	• rain • well pump

7. Sample answer:
Earth is saturated with water just below the surface (white sand). The uppermost area is called the water table (modeling clay). Most of the void spaces in the rocks below the water table are filled with water (small rocks that make hills and valleys). When a water-bearing rock readily transmits water to wells and springs, it is called an aquifer. Wells can be drilled into aquifers and water can be pumped out (straw and pump). Precipitation refills or recharges the aquifers for future water use (spray bottle). Some rocks are more porous than others so rocks store different amounts of water (white sand, clay, and small rocks). The use and recharge of aquifers must be carefully balanced to prevent a well running dry.

8.

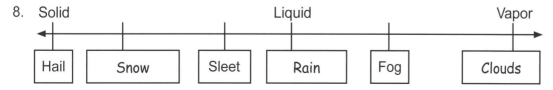

9. Sample answer*:

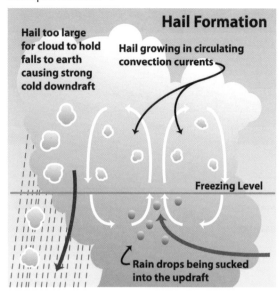

Hail Formation

Hail too large for cloud to hold falls to earth causing strong cold downdraft

Hail growing in circulating convection currents

Freezing Level

Rain drops being sucked into the updraft

10. Answers will vary. Sample answers:

Device	How It Works
Wall clock	helps to time your shower to less than 5 minutes, saving 1,000 gallons of water a month
Ears	help to listen for drips and fix leaks as soon as they're heard

11. Answers will vary.

12. 78 baths

13. Answers will vary.

14. Answers will vary.

15. Answers will vary.

Severe Weather pp. 42-44

1. super cell, non-super cell

2. A storm <u>watch</u> is when there is a possibility of severe weather in an area. A storm <u>warning</u> is when there is definitely severe weather in an area.

3. Wind speed answers will vary because of different scales used, but students' answers should be close to the ranges provided:

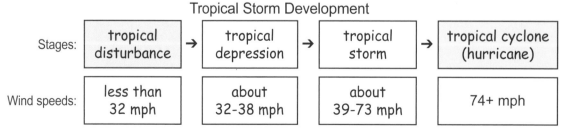

Tropical Storm Development

Stages:	tropical disturbance	→	tropical depression	→	tropical storm	→	tropical cyclone (hurricane)
Wind speeds:	less than 32 mph		about 32-38 mph		about 39-73 mph		74+ mph

* Hail formation illustration from scijinks.nasa.gov/rain

4. hurricanes

5. Chart answers will vary. For a list of retired hurricane names, go to http://www.nhc.noaa.gov/aboutnames_history.shtml.

6. Possible answers:

Spring	Summer	Fall	Winter
• blizzard • fog • hailstorm • ice storm • snowstorm • thunderstorm • tornado	• drought • dust storm • flash flood • fog • heat wave • hurricane • thunderstorm • tornado • tropical storm • wind storm	• drought • flash flood • fog • hurricane • Nor'easter • snowstorm • thunderstorm • tornado • tropical storm • wind storm	• blizzard • fog • ice storm • Nor'easter • snowstorm • thunderstorm

7. The Coriolis effect is the appearance of a projectile, water, or wind current to veer to the right in the Northern Hemisphere and to the left in the Southern Hemisphere due to Earth's rotation on its axis.

8. air pressure

9. Tropical regions would have lower air pressure than polar regions because as air warms up it rises and expands, which lowers the air pressure. At polar regions, the air drops as it cools, creating higher pressure on Earth.

10. cloudy and rainy; possibly strong storms

11. EF5

12. Paragraphs should describe trees down or cut in half, livestock dead in the pastures, tops of houses missing, 39 blocks of town destroyed, 9 human fatalities, many homes reduced to rubble, etc.

13. Sample answers:

Hurricane Survival Tips	Lightning Survival Tips	Flooding Survival Tips	Tornado Survival Tips	Winter Storm Survival Tips
• prepare an emergency kit • get news and weather updates • board up windows • secure large or loose items • stay indoors	• stay indoors • count time between lightning and thunder to determine distance • do not go in water • stay away from tall structures • do not use electric products	• do not cross water • get to higher ground • stay indoors • watch for large objects in water • keep emergency kit	• stay indoors • go to basement or cellar • stay away from windows • get out of car and go to ditch or crouch near building • protect head	• stay indoors • keep car safety kit • dress in layers • keep emergency items nearby • exercise to stay warm

14. flashlight, water, canned foods, batteries, and a radio

Weather Instruments   pp. 45-47

1. ___weather vane___   ___rain gauge___   ___thermometer___; weather vane
        50 BC   AD 1441   AD 1593

2. Athens, Greece, 48 BC

3. relative humidity

4.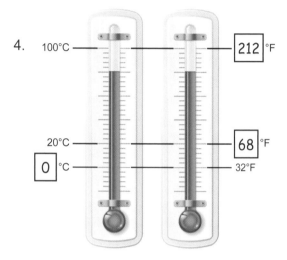

5. Most thermometers are closed glass tubes containing liquids such as alcohol or mercury. When air around the tube heats the liquid, the liquid expands and moves up the tube. A scale then shows what the actual temperature is around the tube.

6. When air around the tube cools the liquid, the liquid contracts and moves down the tube.

7. weather satellites

8.
Clue	Weather Instrument
To get a proper reading, I should be 5 feet above the ground under a shelter.	thermometer or barometer
I usually measure between 28 and 31 inches of mercury.	barometer
I am made of two thermometers (one has a wet cloth on the end).	sling psychrometer
I have several cups that catch the wind and spin around a pole.	anemometer

9-10. Answers will vary based on student's choice.

11. barometer, hygrometer, rain gauge, weather vane, and anemometer

12. Answers will vary based on student's experience in the game.

13. Answers will vary. Weather blimp stories should be creative and include three of the events from the graphic organizer in question 12.

Weather Forecasts   pp. 48-52

1.

Type of Map	Information Shown	Measurements Used
Pressure	• high and low pressure areas	• millibar
Temperature	• past, present, and predicted temperatures	• degrees (Fahrenheit or Celsius)
Station Model	• air pressure • temperature • humidity • cloud cover • wind speed	• millibar • degrees • percents • miles per hour
Aviation	conditions for flying such as: • wind speed • temperature • dew point • fronts • cloud cover • precipitation	• miles per hour • degrees
Streamline	• wind patterns	• isobaric pressure

2.

Types of Air Masses

		Tropical (hot low pressure)	Polar (cold high pressure)
Geographical Features	Maritime (humid ocean)	mT humid, warm, rainy	mP humid, cold, snowy, icy
	Continental (dry land)	cT dry, stable warm air	cP dry, harsh cold air

3.

Reliable Predictors	Unreliable Predictors
• clouds at sunrise or sunset • bees • barometer • curly/frizzy hair	• cows • Grandma's toe

4. When the sun is low, it spreads light through the thickest part of the atmosphere. The sky appears to be red if there are more water and dust particles. Red at night means high-pressure area from the west, so calm weather will follow. Red at morning means the light is reflecting off a storm system moving from the west; the deeper the red the more likely the chance of rain.

5. Map should be labeled using all four types of front symbols.

6. If cold air replaces warm air, it is a cold front; if warm air replaces cold air, it is a warm front.

7. storms causing rain, thunder, lightning, tornadoes, hail, sleet, or snow

8. Answers will vary.

9. Answers will vary.

10. Letters will vary but should use correct friendly letter format and include details from answers 8-9.

Winds   pp. 53-56

1. Katabatic winds blow downslope (from high elevation to low elevation). *Katabatic* means "going downhill."

2.

Wind Name	Location	Name Translation
bora (bura)	Adriatic	"mountain"
Bohemian wind	Ore Mountains	"home"
mistral	Rhone and Durance Valleys (France)	"masterly"
Santa Ana	California	"Saint Ana"
tramontane	Italian Alps	"beyond the mountains"
Oroshi	Japan	"lit, down wind"

3. Chinook wind caused a 30° F increase in temperature within 3 minutes.

4. the Sahara Desert in northern Africa

5. dry desert regions

6. Sample answer:

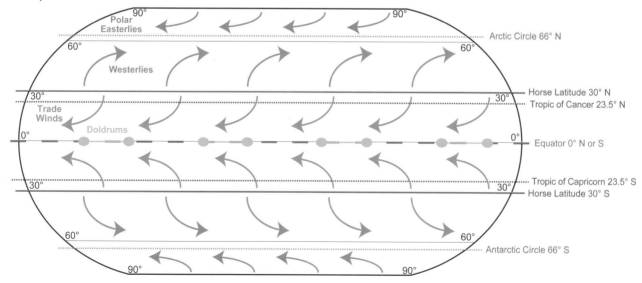

7. There is no wind for lifting the kite on a calm day.

8. Answers will vary.

9. Answers will vary.

10. Answers will vary.

11. The short story should creatively describe the family and their things being blown about from the gale-force winds.

12. Illustrations should contrast the difference between moderate-force winds and gale-force winds.

Section 3 – Ecosystems and Habitats

Deserts   pp. 58-62

1.

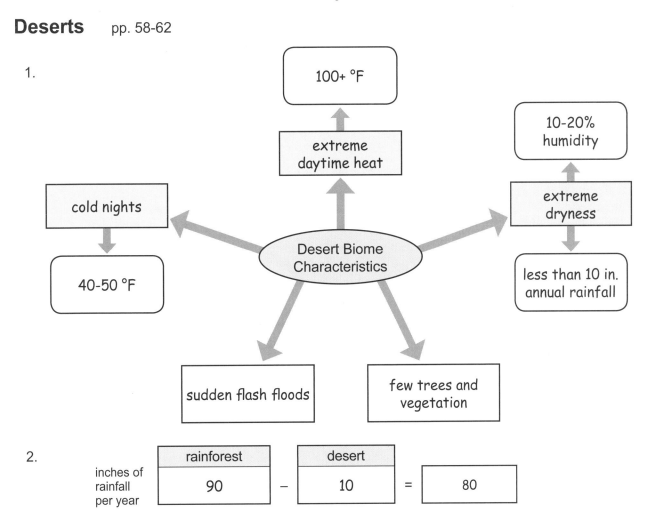

3. Sahara Desert; northern Africa

4. Most deserts are located approximately between 15˚ and 35˚ latitude north and south of the equator.

5.

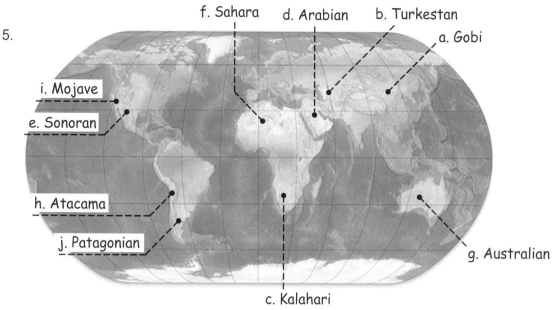

f. Sahara   d. Arabian   b. Turkestan
a. Gobi
i. Mojave
e. Sonoran
h. Atacama
j. Patagonian
g. Australian
c. Kalahari

6. More than 1/5

7. Sample answers:

Adaptation	How it Helps
storing food and water in the animal's body	They can go for days without food and water.
being nocturnal	They don't overheat while hunting.
living underground	They stay cool while hiding from the sun; there is some moisture stored in the ground.
being nomadic	Searching for food in many areas instead of just one means that they have more sources and are less likely to wipe out (or deplete) a food source.

8. Possible answers: deeper roots, special storage and conservation of water, fewer leaves, shorter lifespan, grow only in rainy season

9. Possible answers:

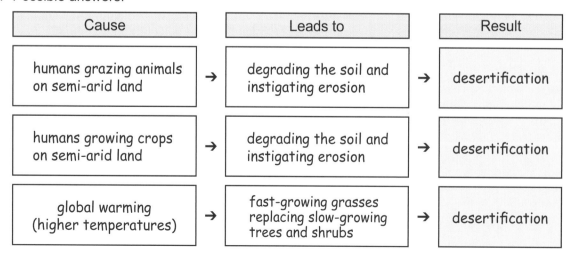

Cause	Leads to	Result
humans grazing animals on semi-arid land	→ degrading the soil and instigating erosion →	desertification
humans growing crops on semi-arid land	→ degrading the soil and instigating erosion →	desertification
global warming (higher temperatures)	→ fast-growing grasses replacing slow-growing trees and shrubs →	desertification

10.

Plants	Animals Living in Herds for Protection	Carnivores (Hunters)
• cactus • palm tree • trees • grass • shrub	• goat • meerkat • gemsbok • emperor penguin • camel	• military sand dragon • gray fox • mountain lion • emperor penguin

11-12. Answers will vary.

Food Webs   pp. 63-65

1. Possible answers: any vegetation native to North America (trees, grass, bushes, flowers, and plants)

2. Possible answers: any animal native to Africa (lion, zebra, elephant, giraffe, monkey, hyena, etc.)

3. Possible answers: any fungi, bacteria, or bug native to Asia (mushrooms, worms, beetles, flies, etc.)

4. Answers will vary. Carnivores eat only meat; examples: any fish, any bird, mice, rabbits, squirrels. Herbivores eat only plants; examples: grass, corn, hay, carrots, oats. Omnivore belongs in the rectangle because they eat both plants and meat.

5. mushrooms, worms, fungi, mold, bacteria

6. Sample answer:
Decomposers break down dead organisms for fertilizing the soil with nutrients for future growth. Without them, the surface of Earth would be covered in dead organisms, no nutrients would fertilize the soil to enable future plant growth so no plants would grow for herbivores and omnivores to eat and no herbivores would grow for carnivores and omnivores to eat. Therefore, all life on Earth would cease to exist without decomposers.

7. Drawing should include pictures in this order:
plant → grasshopper → lizard → eagle → mushrooms → plant

8. Answers will vary. Stories about consumers should include eating plants and/or animals by hunting or grazing, and providing carbon dioxide and balance to ecosystem with population control of plants and animals. Stories about producers should include photosynthesis by getting energy from the sun and providing food and oxygen for animals in ecosystem. Stories about decomposers should include eating dead plants and animals and providing nutrients for the soil in an ecosystem.

Forests   pp. 66-69

1.

	Coniferous Forest	Temperate Deciduous Forest
Definition	Forest mainly consisting of trees that produce cones and needles; some needles remain on trees all year, making it an evergreen forest.	Forest containing broadleaf trees, shrubs, herbs, and mosses going through four seasons where leaves change color, fall off, lay dormant, then grow back.
Locations	Canada, Europe, Asia, United States	Eastern United States, Canada, Europe, China and Japan; Mid-latitude areas between Polar Regions and tropics
Climate	cold, long, snowy winters; humid summers	hot summers; cold winters
Animals	Possible answers: bears, moose, deer, foxes, bobcats, rabbits, rodents, birds, owls, Siberian tiger, snakes	Possible answers: bears, coyotes, deer, rodents, birds, snakes, turkey

2.

Member of Biomes	Bacteria	Water	Green Plant	Bird
Give	break down dead animals and plants	essential life requirement to animals and plants	food, shelter, oxygen	pollinate plants, spread seeds, become food to other animals
Take	nutrients from dead	hydrogen and oxygen	carbon dioxide	eat plants, insects

3. **Air:** Trees absorb carbon dioxide through photosynthesis, produce oxygen, and capture air pollutants.
Wildlife: Forests provide essential habitat for a variety of creatures.
People: Trees remove carbon and give oxygen, provide recreational areas and shade, reduce stress, and increase overall well-being of humans.
Energy: Planting trees saves energy by providing shade to cool areas in summer and exposure to warm areas in winter.

4. Letters will vary but should include benefits of forests, reasons for protection, and ways to prevent forest fires.

5. Answers will vary. Accept any answers that reflect an understanding of recycling, reusing, and reducing waste.

6. Letters will vary but should include the benefits of recycling.

Grasslands   pp. 70-72

1.

	Temperate Grasslands	Tropical Grasslands (Savannas)
Definition	open, continuous flat areas of grass with thick, dark, nutrient-rich soil	open, continuous flat areas of grass with absorbent, quickly draining soil and seasonal fires
Locations	Russia, Africa, North America, South America, Eastern Europe	Africa, India, Australia, South America, Southeastern Asia
Climate	cold winters, warm summers, some rain and snow	warm wet climate; 7-month wet season; hot dry season
Animals	wild horses, bison, rodents, coyotes, badgers, snakes, antelope	elephants, zebras, kangaroos, lions, leopards, deer, emus, koala bears, crocodiles, hyenas, rodents

2. South America: pampa
    North America: prairie
    Africa: savanna
    Eurasia: steppe

3.

Animal	Migrated From	Effect on the Savanna Biome
giraffe	jungle	The acacia tree grew thorns to limit nibbling.
antelope	desert	Trampling feet created open country.
elephant	rain forest	knocked down trees

4. Possible answers:

African Savanna Animals

Mammal	Reptile	Insect	Bird
• baboon • cheetah • elephant • giraffe • hyena • lion • rhinoceros • zebra	• monitor lizard • snake • turtle	• ant • bee • butterfly • dragonfly • dung beetle	• crane • ostrich • starling • vulture

5.
North American Shortgrass Prairie Animals

Birds	Mammals	Amphibians and Reptiles (Herps)
ferruginous hawk	bison	gopher snake
burrowing owl	black-tailed prairie dog	western hognose snake
lesser-prairie chicken	black-footed ferret	racer snake
sandhill crane	Pronghorn	woodhouse toad

6. Answers will vary. Sample:

Adaptation Type	Grassland Location	Example of Adaptation
Human Skill	Cambodia	harvesting snakes in flooded grasslands for food
	Africa	intimidating lions in order to steal their meat
Technology Use	Australia	using helicopters to rustle cattle
Land Use	Argentina	converting grasslands to farmland for cattle, corn, grain, and soy

7. Paragraphs will vary, but should reflect adaptations from question 6.

Oceans   pp. 73-75

1. 70%

2. The euphotic zone is the sunlit zone of the ocean. The sun provides energy for undersea plants and many fish depend on the plants for food and protection.

3. Sample answers:

	Intertidal Zone	Shallow Ocean	Open Ocean	Deep Ocean
Location	along coast; underwater at high tide and above water at low tide	bottom of ocean where it is shallow enough for sunlight to reach	from coast to middle of ocean; largest part of the ocean	bottom of the open ocean where it is very cold; high pressure; no sunlight
Inhabitants	algae, snails, barnds, small fish, mollusks, crustaceans, shrimp, crab, worms	crustaceans, crab, sea stars, snails, fish, sharks, clams, worms, urchins, sea grass, kelp, algae, sea lions, sea otters, coral	plankton, algae, whales, sharks, fish, squid; all living things here must float or swim to survive	clams, mussels, shrimp, crab, tubeworms, fish, bacteria

4. Great Barrier Reef; off the coast of North Eastern Australia; 135,000 sq miles

5. barracudas

6. climate change, pollution, overfishing

7. Possible answers:

Life	"Land" Formations	"Water" Formations

• coral reefs
• jellyfish
• more life, diversity, and density than in the tropical rain forest
• octopus
• vampire squid
	• 80% of Earth's volcanoes
	  › fire
	  › rocks turn to liquid
	• Mid-ocean ridge
	  › mountain range
	  › 50,000 miles long
	• valleys deeper than the Grand Canyon
		• puddle
		• pond
		• sea
		• lake
		• river
		• largest waterfall
		• hot springs

8. Sunlight does not reach the deep ocean, so bioluminescence assists fish as they hunt for food in the deep ocean.

9. Answers will vary but should demonstrate reflection and analysis of possible reasons. Sample answer: Deep ocean animals cannot be collected with a net because these unique jellies and fish are too fragile to be handled with nets and brought to the surface. Special equipment is needed to maintain their pressurized mid-water ecosystem.

10. Answers will vary but should be complete paragraphs containing information from the video.
Sample information:
Dolphins summary: Dolphin moms teach calves to mimic, use echolocation, and hunt for fish in the surf.
Shark summary: Sharks' characteristics of large size, fast speed, great vision, curious mind, and love to taste make sharks the ocean's greatest predator.
Emperor Penguins summary: Penguins survive the harsh cold by banding together, males protecting the eggs while the females hunt, and using speed and agility to escape predators.

Rain Forests   pp. 76-80

1.

Rain Forest	
Definition	tall, dense, tropical jungle that gets 50-260 inches of rain per year
Locations	tropical areas along the equator: Central America, South America, West Africa, Southeastern Asia
Climate	warm, humid
Animals	half the world's plant and animal species (more than 30 million)

2. Pictures will vary but should contain:

Layer	Contents
emergent	tree tops
canopy	giant trees with thick, woody vines preventing much sunlight from reaching the ground
understory	vines, smaller trees, ferns, shrubs, palms
forest floor	wet leaves, leaf litter, compost, soil

3. An Ethiopian goat herder noticed his goats had more energy after eating the berries.

4.
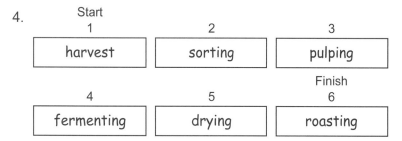

Start
1	2	3
harvest	sorting	pulping

4	5	Finish 6
fermenting	drying	roasting

5. Shade-grown coffee is more sustainable to the environment because it does not require cutting of rain forest trees.

6. cacao tree

7.
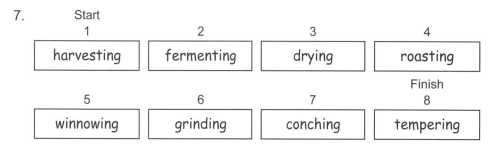

Start
1	2	3	4
harvesting	fermenting	drying	roasting

5	6	7	Finish 8
winnowing	grinding	conching	tempering

8. Sample answers:

Canadian Temperate Rain Forest

Commercial Logging Goals	Environmental Conservationist Goals
• business • provide a commodity/resource for building	• protect green, lush thousand-years-old trees (cedar, spruce, hemlock) • protect wildlife such as cougars, wolves, salmon, grizzly bears • protect the Kermode "Spirit" bear, which is unique to the area • not stripping the mountain

9. Paragraphs will vary but should reflect the information in question 8.

10. Answers will vary. Sample answer: titan arum; only blooms every thousand days, bloom lives for only three days, smells like rotting fish, six foot center spike/piston.

11. Answers will vary. The animals that live only in the rain forest include:

Mammals		Birds	Reptiles

agile gibbon
bald uakari
black-crested gibbon
bonobo
Bornean orangutan
common wooly monkey
Doria's tree-kangaroo
dwarf and
  mouse lemurs
Eastern gorilla
fork-marked lemurs
François' langur
	grey langurs
	indri
	Lar gibbon
	Matschie's
	  tree-kangaroo
	Phayre's leaf monkey
	red ruffed lemur
	silky sifaka
	Sumatran orangutan
	tarsiers
	three-toed sloths
	Western gorilla
		blue bird of paradise
		harpy eagle
		king bird of paradise
		magnificent bird of
		  paradise
		marvellous spatuletail
		Raggiana bird of
		  paradise
		rockfowl
		six-wired bird of paradise
		superb bird of paradise
		Vogelkop bowerbird
			eyelash viper

			Amphibians
			Panamanian golden frog poison dart frog
			Insects/Arachnids
			army ant Goliath bird-eating spider

12. Answers will vary.

13. Paragraphs will vary but should include details of travel during wet or dry seasons, include activities such as view volcanoes, animals, swimming, zip lining through rain forest canopy, surfing, etc. and list animals such as: howler monkeys, macaws, toucans, white faced Capac, Quetzals, tapirs, frogs, snakes, etc.

Taiga and Tundra   pp. 81-82

1.

	Taiga	Tundra
Definition	world's largest land biome; characterized by coniferous forests	low temperatures; short growing season; very few trees; permafrost soil
Locations	Alaska, Canada, Russia, Mongolia, Norway, Sweden, Iceland, and Finland; about 50°-70° N latitude	Arctic tundra (northern Alaska, Canada, and Siberia) and Antarctic tundra; high mountain tops
Climate	below freezing half the year; lots of snow; short, humid summers with temperatures getting up to about 70° F	6-10 week summer; cold year-round (below 50° F); windy
Animals	moose, reindeer, caribou, elk, deer, bison, beaver, hare, bear, Siberian tiger, carrion birds	Arctic fox, caribou, musk ox, Norway lemming, polar bear, snowy owl, tundra swan, seals

2. The taiga is mostly trees, mainly tall trees with deep roots. The tundra is characterized by permafrost soil with almost no trees.

3. Permafrost is the impenetrable layer below the top soil that remains frozen, preventing plant roots from growing deep, so only small plants, shrubs, and mosses can grow.

4. Cone-shaped limbs promote shedding of snow; needles have smaller surface area for water evaporation; darker colors of trees absorb more heat from the sun; evergreen foliage means photosynthesis year-round.

5. thick, furry coats; seasonal migration; seasonal hibernation

6. endothermic bodies/warm-blooded animals

7. change appearance to match season; small compact bodies with extra fat, fur, and feathers; seasonal migration

8. Drawings of taiga and tundra will vary.

9. Narrative stories will vary.

Section 4 – Energy

Electromagnetism   pp. 84-86

1. strong, weak, electromagnetic, and gravity (gravitational)

2. electromagnetism

3. protons, electrons

4. Positive charge has more protons; negative charge has more electrons.

5. An electric current is a flow of charge all going in the same direction.

6. Insulators are materials in which electrons cannot move easily from place to place. Conductors are materials in which electrons can move easily from place to place.

7. A magnet is any object that attracts iron and produces an external magnetic field.

8. Opposite poles attract and same poles repel; the earth's magnetic field makes the compass' internal magnet orient it to the North Pole.

9. The magnets on the car as it falls create a magnetic field on the tube that is opposite the magnets on the car making it stop. This is called eddy current braking.

10. Electricity gets its name from the flow of electrons moving from conductor to conductor.

11. When an object containing iron attaches to a magnet, its domains line up and can attract other objects.

12. generator

13. Sample answer: An electromagnet with a fixed shaft in its center turns to align with the poles of a horseshoe magnet with an electric current is sent. When the poles align, a switch called a commentator reverses the flow of electricity through the electromagnet causing the poles to reverse its alignment. Constant switching of the electric current causes the electromagnet to spin creating energy to power a machine thus converting electric energy into mechanical energy.

14. Increased voltage sends more power through the circuit, which increases the brightness of the light.

15. Increased length of wire increases the resistance to the current, which decreases the brightness of the light.

16.

battery	motor	buzzer	connector	open switch
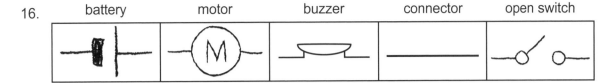

17. Pictures will vary but should include the symbols from question 16.

Energy and Conservation   pp. 87-89

1. Energy is the ability to do work.

2. Kinetic = moving energy
   Potential = stored energy

3.

Form of Energy	Characteristics	Example
Thermal (Heat) Energy	The collective kinetic and potential energy of molecules in an object, measured in temperature; the higher the temperature, the faster the molecules are moving and storing energy.	hot cup of coffee (or anything hot)
Chemical Energy	A form of microscopic potential energy; exists because of the forces of attraction between molecules causing chemical reactions.	glucose releasing energy in a body; battery (or any chemical reaction)
Electrical Energy	Electrons moving among atoms forming an electric current; measured in volts; materials have conductivity or resistance to electricity.	electrical outlets, switches (or any substance carrying an electrical current)
Sound Energy	Compression waves of the potential and kinetic energy of air molecules.	head of a drum compressing and expanding air (or anything that makes sound)

4. Sample answer:
   Conduction transmits heat energy by vibrating particles. Conduction would be used to cook popcorn in a pot with a lid on a stovetop. The heat source would increase the movement of the molecules in the pot, which would then increase the movement in the molecules in the oil and popcorn.
   Convection transmits heat energy by moving liquid or gas. Convection cooks popcorn in a hot air popper by circulating heated air.
   Radiation transfers energy through electromagnetic waves. Microwave ovens use radiation to cook the popcorn kernels.
   All three methods cook the popcorn by converting the water inside the kernels to steam, which expands the starch inside the kernels into puffed air starch.

5. Illustrations will vary but should include:

biomass	geothermal	hydropower	solar	wind
sun stored in plants	energy from within Earth (volcanoes, geysers, springs, etc.)	flowing water or rain	sunshine	wind

211

6. Sample answer: The Law of Conservation of Energy states that energy cannot be created or destroyed, so when the bowling ball is pulled back (potential energy) and released (kinetic energy), it cannot go farther than it is pulled back — therefore, not hitting the person who releases it.

7. Conservation is the practice of decreasing the amount of energy used.

8. Possible answers: costs rise for precious energy sources remaining; no energy sources remaining; environment greatly damaged or destroyed

9. Sample answers:

Change	How it Conserves Energy
Keep vents clear and clean.	It takes less energy to pump air through.
Ceiling fan direction; turn it off when you're out of the room.	The direction pushes cold air down or keeps hot air up; a fan uses no energy when it is off.
Caulk/weather strip windows.	less energy for temperature control
Unplug chargers and cords when not in use.	uses no energy
Turn lights off when you leave a room.	uses no energy

Fossil Fuels   pp. 90-92

1. Fossil fuels were formed over millions of years by heat and pressure turning decomposing remains of plants and animals into fuel (oil, coal, and natural gas).

2. coal, oil*, natural gas*

3.

Fossil Fuels	Oil	Coal	Natural Gas
Impact From **Extracting** From Earth	Large holes are drilled. Oil spills from drilling damage habitat and animals.	Strip mining destroys habitat and leaves big pits in the ground.	Large holes are drilled. Gas leaks are lethal to surrounding animals.
Impact From **Burning** for Energy	Emits greenhouse gases like carbon dioxide, methane, and sulfur oxide into the atmosphere.	Emits CO_2, a major cause of climate change. Mercury contamination, ozone pollution, and acid rain also stem from the firing of coal.	Emits less greenhouse gases than coal or oil. Main cause of methane leaks.

4. Answers will vary; for a longer list, go to http://www.ranken-energy.com/Products%20from%20Petroleum.htm.
   Sample answers: gasoline, diesel fuel, kerosene, tar, chemicals for plastic

5. Fossil fuels are the cheapest source of energy.

6.

Step	Location	Function
1	coal yard	stores coal
2	conveyor belt	brings coal into the plant
3	pulverizer	grinds coal into powder
4	furnace	burns coal
5	boiler tubes	heat water into steam (from the heat of the furnace)
6	large pipes	transfers steam at high speed and pressure to turbine
7	turbine	steam pushes turbine blades, causing them to spin
8	generator rotor	spins from the turbine blades and creates flow of electrons
9	stator	produces electricity from the spinning rotor
10	transformers	send electricity to power lines
11	power lines	send electricity to homes and businesses

7.

	Coal	Oil
New Methods of **Removing** the Fossil Fuel	bucket wheel excavator	floating oil rigs (like the Eirik Raude)
How it Works	Removes massive amounts of coal and redistributes the soil for reuse.	Six thrusters hold oil rig in place while massive drill at center of rig retrieves oil from seabed.

8. Answers will vary. Example: The new advances in removing fossil fuels from the earth include floating deep water oil rigs and coal bucket excavators. A deep water oil rig is a floating city around a massive oil drill. Some benefits of the floating deep water drill are: it is the most versatile oil rig ever by being able to drill in deeper waters in any weather. A coal bucket excavator is a fast mechanized digging system to remove coal from the ground. Some benefits of the bucket excavator are more environmentally responsible by redistributing the topsoil after removing the coal and it utilizes a home-grown energy source for the United States. Disadvantages of removing fossil fuels from the earth include: they add billions of tons of carbon dioxide to the atmosphere and may disrupt ecosystems where they are drilling.

Hydroelectricity   pp. 93-95

1. Hydroelectricity is electricity generated by the gravitational power of falling water. It is a renewable resource.

2. Hydroelectric power plants reuse pumped stored water during peak power hours to quickly add water to turn turbines.

3. Three Gorges Dam; Yangtze River, China (as of 2013)

4. Grand Coulee Dam; Columbia River, Washington (as of 2013)

5. Answers will vary.

6. Sample answer:

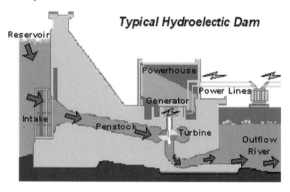

Typical Hydroelectic Dam

7. Answers will vary but should include these steps:
The hydroelectric plant generates electricity from gravitational energy of water to turn turbines and (Step 1) sends the electric power to transmission substations in order to (Step 2) increase the voltage (Step 3) to travel long distances over transmission line towers. Next, (Step 4) the voltage is lowered at a subtransmission station as it nears a city and (Step 5) is sent closer to homes and businesses over subtransmission line towers. Then, (Step 6) the voltage is lowered a final time at a distribution station and (Step 7) sent over wooden distribution power poles directly to homes and places of business.

8.

Hoover Dam Facts

Main Construction Material Used	River Feeding the Dam
Concrete	Colorado River
Years Construction Began and Completed	Number of Generators
1931-1936	17
Height	Power Capacity – Number of Households
726 ft	1,700,000 households

9. Transmission substations increase the voltage of electricity to be carried over extra high voltage transmission towers; distribution stations lower the voltage a second time to safely transmit electricity over distribution poles to homes.

Nuclear Energy   pp. 96-100

1.

	Nuclear Fusion	Nuclear Fission
How is the energy released?	Energy is released when atoms are combined or fused together to form a larger atom.	Atoms are split apart to form smaller atoms, releasing energy.
What uses this process to produce energy?	The sun produces energy through fusion.	Nuclear power plants use nuclear fission to produce electricity.

2. Nuclear reactors are basically machines that contain and control chain reactions while releasing heat from the fission process at a controlled rate.

3.

Isotope Definition	
An isotope is an element (atom) with an equal number protons but a different number of neutrons.	
Health Risks Linked to Uranium Isotopes	Uses for Uranium Isotopes
• lung cancer • bone cancer • kidney damage • infertility • miscarriages • leukemia	• nuclear weapons • nuclear power • nuclear reactors

4. approximately 20%

5. atomic bomb

6. Sample answers:

Nuclear Energy Pros	Nuclear Energy Cons
• produces no smoke • carbon free • produces more electricity for less cost than solar, wind, and coal • uses less land • better for preventing global warming	• uranium must be mined • dangerous radioactive waste • high maintenance costs for plants • fears of nuclear weapons being made from enriched uranium • safety concerns after the 1979, 1986, and 2011 nuclear plant disasters • toxic waste ruins land for future use • radiation increases the risk of cancer

7. Answers will vary but should contain supporting pros and cons from question 6.

8. Sample answer*:

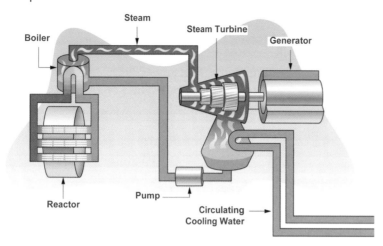

9. The basic steps in the nuclear power plant cycle are:

1.	Heat is created through the fission in the reactor.
2.	Heavy water is circulated and heated through the nuclear reaction in the reactor.
3.	Heated heavy water travels to the boiler where it converts normal water to steam.
4.	The steam is used to turn a turbine.
5.	The turbine spins a rotor of a large electromagnet in the generator.
6.	The generator produces electricity that is moved across transmission lines to homes and buildings.
7.	The steam is condensed back into water using cooling water from a nearby source and pumped back to boilers to continue the process.

10. Sample answers:

Nuclear Meltdowns

Three Mile Island	Chernobyl	Fukushima
• March 28, 1979 • near Harrisburg, Pa. • pressure built up in the reactor due to failed water pumps causing a valve to open • workers did not see signal that valve was open, causing fuel rods to overheat and partially melt down • no deaths occurred	• April 26, 1986 • About 80 miles north of Kiev, Ukraine • a test caused a big power surge due to a design flaw in the reactor • workers had not shut down the core prior to the test, so the nuclear reaction went out of control, causing two major explosions • no containment structure around the reactor allowed radioactive material into the atmosphere, causing 28 early deaths and putting thousands at risk for cancer	• March 11, 2011 • Fukushima prefecture, about 150 miles north of Tokyo on Japan's northeastern coast • an earthquake caused a tsunami to flood the power plant and knock out its electricity • without cool water circulating, the fuel rods overheated, causing a massive meltdown • explosions of released gas breached the containment vessels, allowing radioactive materials to escape

* Used with permission from Ontario Power Generation Inc.

11. Answers will vary but should reflect the information in question 10.

12. Raise and lower control rods, increase primary water coolant, increase secondary water coolant

13. Answers will vary.

Solar and Wind Energy   pp. 101-103

1.

	Solar Energy	Wind Power
Definition	a renewable resource that is created by the transformation of heat energy from the sun into electricity	a renewable resource that is created by the movement of air
Largest "Farm" in the World Location as of 2013	Agua Caliente Solar Project, Yuma County, Arizona (as of October 2013)	Alta Wind Energy Center, Kern County, California (as of October 2013)

2. Sample answer: The <u>wind</u> flows over the blades creating lift, which causes them to rotate. The blades are connected to a <u>drive shaft</u> that turns an electric <u>generator</u> to produce <u>electricity</u>.

3. heat water, spaces, fluids

4. Phovaltaic cells are built to absorb photons from sunlight. When the phovaltaic cells absorb enough photons, electrons are dislodged from the material and move to the front surface of the phovaltaic cell creating an imbalance in the cells charge. One surface contains more negatively charged electrons and the other surface contains more positively charged protons. Then, the phovaltaic cell transmits electricity just like a battery.

5. At solar-thermal/electric power plants, solar energy is used to heat fluid to very high temperatures. The fluid is circulated through pipes to transfer the heat energy to water to produce steam. Then, the steam is converted into mechanical energy to turn a turbine in a generator to produce electricity.

6. tops of smooth, rounded hills; open plains; shorelines; mountain gaps

7. Since heat is <u>absorbed</u> in cities because of the dark color of buildings, dark pavement, and the "maze" layout, people have to use more electricity to cool their homes and businesses in warm climates. If homes and businesses were lighter colors, then they would <u>reflect</u> the heat and occupants would use less electricity to cool the buildings in warm climates. In cold climates, having darker buildings would save energy for heating because they would <u>absorb</u> the sun's heat.

8. Possible answers:
   • creates very little carbon monoxide and smog
   • net metering allows citizens to sell electricity to utility companies
   • renewable resource
   • more energy falls as sunlight on the U.S. in a single day than it uses in a year
   • solar panels provide shade
   • reduces price per unit of electricity
   • captures enough energy to meet the electric needs of ½ million people
   • can be used despite the weather

9. Possible answers:
   - supplies energy to the school
   - makes money for school when it sells extra energy
   - learning lab on school property
   - saves trees
   - low carbon emissions

10. Possible answers:
   - expensive to build
   - must be high wind zone
   - wind unpredictable
   - wind field affects wildlife

11. Answers will vary but should reflect the information in questions 9-10.

Section 5 – Geology

Erosion and Weathering   pp. 105-108

1. Erosion is the removal of solid material by the force of rain or wind.

2. rainfall

3. tiny particles of sediment

4. Colorado River

5.

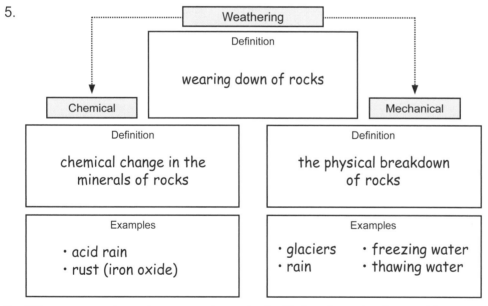

6. When oxygen in water comes in contact with iron in rocks, iron oxide or rust, is formed and weakens the rock.

7. sulfuric acid

8. Rocks worn down by abrasion during the erosion process will eventually become sand.

9. Loss of vegetation increases erosion's destruction by washing away the soil at a rapid rate, which increases the chance of flash floods and whole mountainsides eroding into the valleys below.

10. Image should show glacier formed landscape — i.e., greatly sloped mountains with sharp ridges, huge culverts or steep drops; may be snow or vegetation covered.

11. Creative writing will vary but should include details about living in a glacier-formed landscape.

12. a. Hypotheses will vary; should include guess on how slope, rain and vegetation will affect erosion. In any order:

Slope Gradient (degrees)	Vegetation?	Rain Intensity	Sediment Level	↑↓
30°	Yes	Low	3	
30°	Yes	High	6	
30°	No	Low	7	
30°	No	High	9	↑
10°	Yes	Low	2	↓
10°	Yes	High	5	
10°	No	Low	6	
10°	No	High	8	

b. Students should note if the hypothesis statement was correct or not.
c. Students should conclude that a higher slope, lack of vegetation, and high intensity of rain create greater erosion effects in the landscape.

Minerals pp. 109-112

1. Minerals are solid, inorganic substances found on Earth.

2. Minerals are single substance; rocks are composed of two or more minerals.

3. • color
   • cleavage or fracture
   • tenacity
   • odor
   • streak
   • crystalline structure
   • magnetism
   • taste
   • hardness
   • diaphaneity or amount of transparency
   • luster
   • specific gravity

4. **Mohs Relative Hardness Scale**

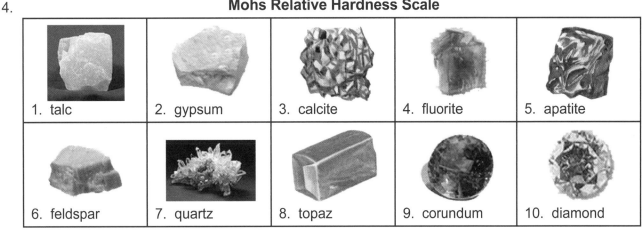

1. talc	2. gypsum	3. calcite	4. fluorite	5. apatite
6. feldspar	7. quartz	8. topaz	9. corundum	10. diamond

5.

1.	formed by natural processes
2.	inorganic
3.	solid
4.	distinct chemical composition
5.	unique repeating atomic pattern

6. Answers will vary.

7. Sample answers for Venn diagram:

Mineral	Both	Cake
• naturally occurring • inorganic • ordered atomic arrangement	• solid • definite chemical compositions	• made by people • disorderly atomic arrangement

8. Minerals: quartz, gold, hematite, icebergs

9. Ozark Mountains of Missouri

10. Possible answers: mining takes place more than 1,000 feet below ground; workers have high risk of lead poisoning.

11. Answers will vary but should explain their choices.

Rocks   pp. 113-115

1.

Classes of Rocks

Igneous	Sedimentary	Metamorphic
Formed by	Formed by	Formed by
molten lava and magma cooling	rocks worn away by wind and water, forming tiny particles which are compressed over time to form layer after layer	other rocks are changed due to heat and pressure
Examples (will vary)	Examples (will vary)	Examples (will vary)
• andesite • basalt • diorite • granite • obsidian	• argillite • chalk • claystone • coal • limestone	• anthracite • blueschist • marble • mylonite • slate

2. sedimentary

3. igneous

4. limestone

5. Possible answers: basalt, anorthosite, breccia, norite, troctolite, pristine highland rock, and regolith

6. They have learned the early history of the moon and possible theories to its formation. They have learned the chemical composition of the moon and solar activity since the formation of the moon.

7. They hope to learn the history of other planets through the study of rocks.

8. Sample answer:

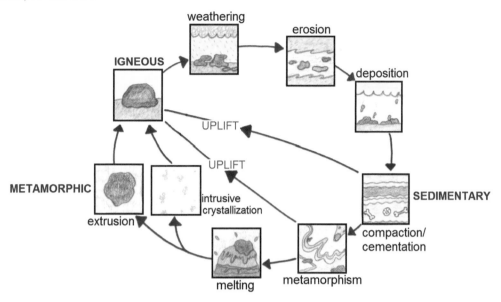

9. Sample answers:
    • <u>molten rock</u> can cool above or below ground
    • <u>plume of volcanic gases</u> where the lava reaches the south shore
    • lava adds to the island's size each day
    • molten lava is less dense than water, so it <u>floats</u>
    • when it cools, it is denser than water, so it <u>sinks</u>
    • <u>extrusive igneous rock</u> forms above ground
    • <u>intrusive igneous rock</u> forms below ground without ever reaching the earth's surface
    • intrusive igneous rock forms <u>lava tubes</u>; when the ground caves in, the lava flow can be explored

10. Paragraphs will vary, but should include descriptions of hot lava hitting the ocean and rapidly cooling to form igneous rocks. Some rocks float to other locations and some rocks harden and sink to form new land on the island. Extrusive igneous rocks form outside the volcano; intrusive igneous rocks form inside the volcano in underground lava flows.

Plate Tectonics   pp. 116-119

1. Plate tectonics refer to the geological theory that Earth's lithosphere (crust and mantle) is divided into sections called plates whose movements explain the phenomena of earthquakes, volcanoes, and mountain formations.

2.

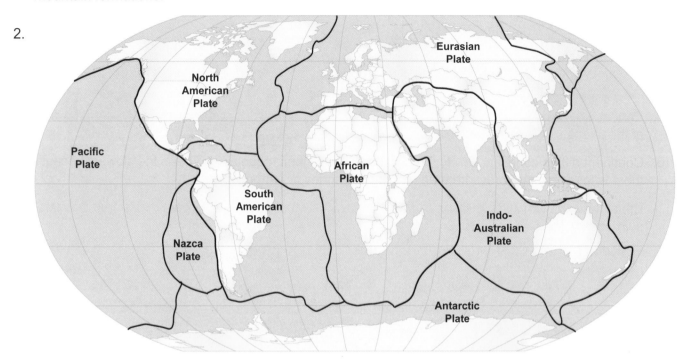

3. Earthquakes occur as transform boundaries grind past each other because the fault lines where two plates meet are rough and get stuck while the rest of the plate keeps moving. Finally, when the plates move far enough, the land unsticks rapidly, causing an earthquake.

4. Underwater volcanoes created by divergent plate boundaries in the oceanic rift create new land on the ocean floor.

5.

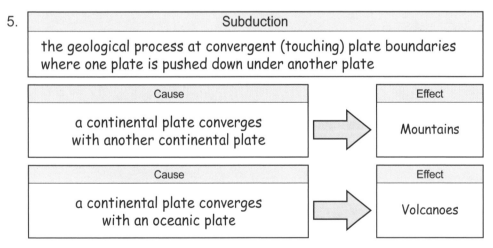

6. Pangaea was a super continent containing all the seven continents.

7. Plate tectonics split it apart to let heat escape Earth.

8.

Boundary Name	Convergent	Transform	Divergent
Action of Plates	Continental hits continental; oceanic slides under continental; oceanic slides under oceanic.	Continental or oceanic plates slip past other plates.	Oceanic or continental plates pull away from other plates.
Effects of Action	Mountains, volcanoes, and oceanic trenches formed.	earthquakes	Rifts form as new crust is added.

9. Earthquakes cause the most rapid damage because of the buildup of pressure and little to no warning of the event.

10. Continent hitting continent slowly forces land to rise to form mountains. This is the slowest because there is less heat and pressure than forming volcanoes or earthquakes.

11. Earth stays the same size because of the constant balance between divergent boundaries pushing out new crust and convergent

12. Sample answers:

Subduction (Convergent)	Strike/Slip (Transform)	Uplifting (Convergent)
(collide) • volcanoes • Mt. Whitney • Mt. Shasta • Andes mountain range • mid-ocean ridges • underwater volcanic chains	(plates move by one another) • tip over buildings • earthquakes • help us to define plate boundaries • San Andreas Fault	• seaside cliffs

13. Answers will vary, but should have descriptions of underwater volcanoes, earthquake destruction, or the formation of cliffs and mountains.

Earthquakes   pp. 120-125

1. Earth's crust is divided into large, shifting sections or plates. Faults form near plate boundaries where the transform collision of two plates causes earthquakes along fault lines.

2. The hypocenter of an earthquake is the focus of the rock rupture at the fault underground. The epicenter is the point on the surface directly above the hypocenter and experiences the most damage.

3. on average, 2,600 per day

4. Alaska; 7,158 (12,053 − 4,895 = 7,158)

5.

6.

Before	During	After
Plates move against each other; friction at boundaries builds up pressure at fault lines.	Stress gives way at faults causing rapid movement. Energy moves through Earth in the form of seismic waves.	Earth may crack, property damaged, and lives lost. Greater damage with earthquakes higher on Richter Scale.

7. Scientists measure earthquakes' seismic waves on a device called a seismograph, which creates lines based on the movement of Earth's crust. Scientists rate the magnitude or force of the earthquake by measuring the length of the lines on the Richter scale. For an earthquake to measure one number higher on the Richter scale, it must release 30 times more energy than the number below it.

8. Engineers and architects study earthquakes in order to better design buildings, roads, bridges and other structures to withstand the movement of the ground beneath them.

9.

Natural Disaster

Date	Location
March 11, 2011	80 miles east offshore of Sendai, Japan

Size
9.0 magnitude

Earthquake Tsunami

Size
massive waves reached 3 miles inland

Damages
• building foundations shaken • celings fell • furniture damaged, broken, or crushed • tsunami wave created

Damages
• 28,000 people died • hit many cities on east coast of Japan • buildings/cities destroyed • cars, homes and property washed away

10. When two tectonic plates collide releasing enormous energy, the earthquakes that occur on the ocean floor displace massive amounts of water creating tsunami waves in all directions from the epicenter of the earthquake.

11.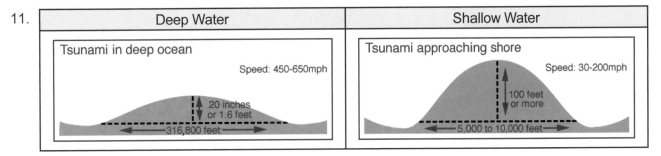

12. Answers will vary.
Sample Effective Defenses: retrofit old buildings to new building codes, install seismic measurement system, install evacuation alarm system, conduct evacuation training, build hospital, build school, house all people
Sample Ineffective Defenses: building on sandy ground, no alarm system or evacuation training, not enough secure housing, no hospital to treat injured, old buildings not brought up to code

13. Answers will vary but should include students' creative ideas on how to protect cities from earthquake and tsunami damage based on their experiments with the simulation.

14. Offshore Sumatra in the Indian Ocean; 9.1 magnitude; 14 countries affected

15. Chile; May 22, 1960; 9.5

16. Answers will vary. Sample answer:
A geophysicist is a person who studies Earth using gravity, magnetic, electrical, and seismic measurements. Geophysicists spend lots of time outdoors studying Earth's features, but also study from the indoors with many tools and computers. They evaluate Earth for minerals, sources of fossil fuels, and/or environmental hazards for building dams, bridges, and cities. They also study Earth to predict future earthquakes, tsunamis, and volcanic eruptions.

Volcanoes   pp. 126-130

1. openings or vents to the heat of Earth

2. band of volcanoes surrounding the Pacific Plate

3. Lava is above ground melted rock. Magma is underground melted rock.

4. Hawaii; Mt Kilauea; It is a shield volcano.

5.

Cinder Cone	Composite Volcano
Magma Vent Fine ash Cinder	Ash Vent Magma Lava Branch pipe
Shield Volcano	Lava Dome
Vent Gentle slope of basaltic lava flow Magma	Vent Steep convex slope from thick, fast-cooling lava Magma

6. 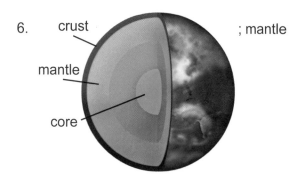   ; mantle

7.

At Constructive Plate Boundaries	At Destructive Plate Boundaries	In the Middle of Plates
Hot magma forces plates apart forming a volcano to release Earth's energy.	As one plate is dragged beneath another plate, friction releasing massive energy to melt the rock and form volcanoes.	Hot spots form where hot rocks from near Earth's core rise up through the mantle and melt near the crust, and then push through the crust forming volcanic islands.

8. Hawaii is a chain of islands with several active volcanoes. They are evidence that as the Pacific Plate moves across the hot spot it forms new volcanoes.

9. Its lava is very runny with lots of water vapor bubbling up inside. This vapor creates splashes of molten lava that are beautiful to watch.

10. Viscosity is how thick and sticky the lava is; the amount of silica in the lava determines viscosity.

11. hydrochloric acid, carbon monoxide, hydrofluoric acid

12. Lots of water causes an explosive eruption. Little water causes an oozing lava flow.

13.

	The AD 79 Eruption of Italy's Mt. Vesuvius (buried the entire city of Pompeii under ash, preserving it for all time)	The 1883 Eruption of Indonesia's Mt. Krakatau (created a blast heard 3,000 miles away that completely broke the volcanic mountain apart)
Effect on Landscape	Covered entire city in ash.	Destroyed volcanic island; tsunamis engulfed coastlines of Indonesia.
Effect on Wildlife	Destroyed all within eruption zone.	Destroyed all within eruption zone; covered surrounding islands in hot ash.
Effect on Cities	Completely buried city of Pompeii.	Coastline cities engulfed in water; ash carried hundreds of miles.
Effect on Humans	Everyone died due to no notice of eruption and close proximity to volcano.	Thousands died, mainly from tsunamis and hot ash.
Effect on Weather	No known effects.	Temperature of Earth cooled; color of sky changed for months.

Sample paragraphs:

   In AD 79, Mt. Vesuvius covered the city of Pompeii in poisonous ash, killing all living things in their tracks. The city was buried for years and when discovered, the mummified remains told the tragic story of the super volcano's destructive force.

   In 1883, Mt. Krakatau erupted for more than two days, ending in a cataclysmic event that blew up the entire mountain. The eruptions caused earthquakes and tsunamis, killing thousands on nearby islands. The final eruption was heard 3,000 miles away and ash from the explosion traveled around the world.

Section 6 – Plants

Plants   pp. 132-137

1. Sample answers for Venn diagram:

Plants	Both	Animals
• cannot move (relocate) • no mouth for eating • gets its nourishment from its root system, which holds it in place • takes carbon dioxide from the air and releases oxygen	• living • need water to live • lay eggs • both can be food for animals	• moves and hunts to find food • consumes food through mouths • takes in oxygen from the air and releases carbon dioxide

2. Answers will vary. Accept any reasonable use of plant for animals: oxygen, food, shelter, paper products, fuel, clothing, etc.

3.

	Angiosperm	Gymnosperm
Definition	Any plant that produces flowers and encloses its seeds in a fruit.	Any non-flowering plant whose seeds are exposed, including conifers and cycads.
Examples	Answers will vary; accept any flowering plant such as: • rose • lily • apple tree • daffodil • tomato plant	Answers will vary; accept any non-flowering plant that is not a moss or fern such as: • pine trees • gingko • cycads • cedar trees • spruce trees

4. Sample answers:

The Facts of Case 1

Plant Structure	Plant Parts	Life Cycle	Growing Plants Indoors
• Herbaceous or woody stems	Roots • get nutrients from soil Stem • disperses nutrients to leaves Leaves • food-making factory; photosynthesis Flower • makes seeds during fertilization Fruit • contains seeds Seeds • new/baby plants	Annual • grows, flowers, sets seed and dies in one year Biennial • grows leaves first year/ flowers and seeds and dies next year Perennial • lives 3 or more years	All plants need: • room to grow • the right temperature • water • air • nutrients • time • sunlight • soil/nutrients

5. Woody plants have stems that are hard and usually do not die back to the ground every year. Woody plants are used to make furniture. Herbaceous plants with non-woody stems die back to the ground every year.

6.

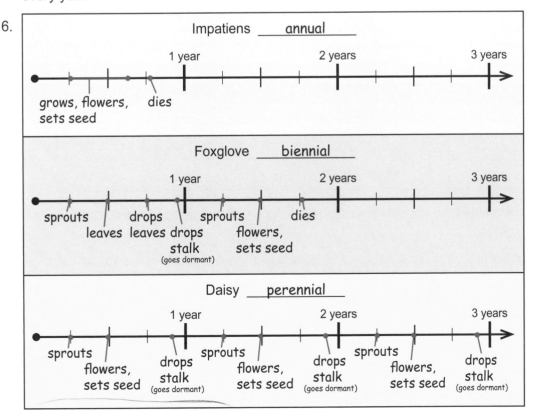

7. Stems will be thin and the plant will lean toward the light.

8. Sample answers:

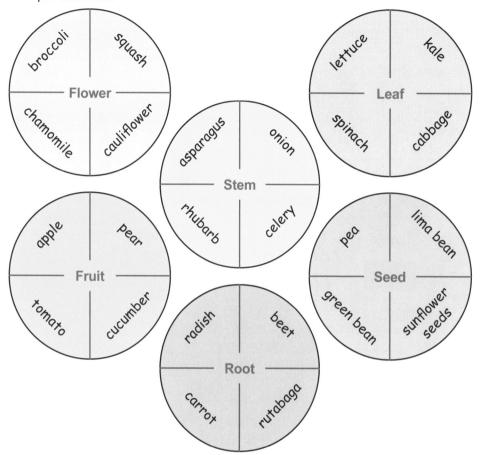

9.

Non-Mineral Nutrients	Mineral Nutrients	
1. hydrogen (H)	1. nitrogen (N)	8. copper (Cu)
2. oxygen (O)	2. phosphorus (P)	9. iron (Fe)
3. carbon (C)	3. potassium (K)	10. chloride (Cl)
	4. calcium (Ca)	11. manganese (Mn)
	5. magnesium (Mg)	12. molybdenum (Mo)
	6. sulfur (S)	13. zinc (Zn)
	7. boron (B)	

10. In photosynthesis, plants use the non-minerals carbon dioxide and hydrogen to create starches and sugars for plant energy.

11. Farmers and gardeners user fertilizer to ensure all the necessary nutrients are in the soil for plant growth.

12. Paragraph should describe ways of obtaining: ideal soil texture contains equal parts sand, silt, clay, and organic matter and ideal soil pH is in the range of 6.0 to 6.5. May add lime or fertilizer to ensure ideal soil.

13.

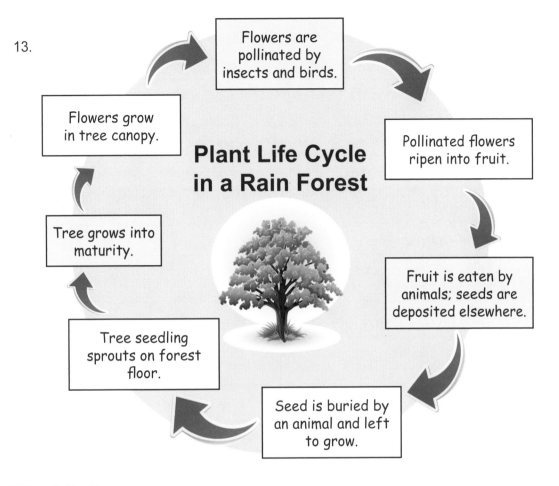

Plant Cells   pp. 138-141

1. Chlorophyll is the pigment that gives plants their green color. It is a molecule that can use light energy from sunlight to turn water and carbon dioxide gas into sugar and oxygen.

2. Photosynthesis is the process by which green plants turn energy from the sun into food for the plant.

3. Plant cells that conduct photosynthesis are located in the leaves of a plant.

4. Sample answers for Venn diagram:

Plant Cells	Both	Animal Cells
• cell walls • chloroplasts • large, central vacuoles	• eukaryotic cells with nucleus • membrane-bound organelles	• centrioles

5.

Cell Part	Function
cell wall	surrounds and protects the cell and gives it structure
plasma membrane	lining of the cell beneath the cell wall; controls what molecules go in and out of cell
chloroplast	converts the sun's light into energy (ATP) for the cell through photosynthesis
cytoplasm	fluid that fills the cell; all organelles are floating in this fluid
endoplasmic reticulum	surrounds the nucleus; readies protein for transport to other parts of the cell
Golgi apparatus	groups lipids and proteins into packages for transport to other parts of cell or plant
mitochondria	produces ATP (energy) from glucose to fuel the plant
nucleus	holds a complete set of genes (DNA) and directs the activity of the cell
ribosome	follows instructions given by nucleus and produces proteins
vacuole	stores vital water and nutrients; also stores waste; holds cell structure- causes leaves to look large and point upward when full of water or droop when lacking water
peroxisomes	converts stored oils into molecules that can be used for energy

6.

PLANT CELL

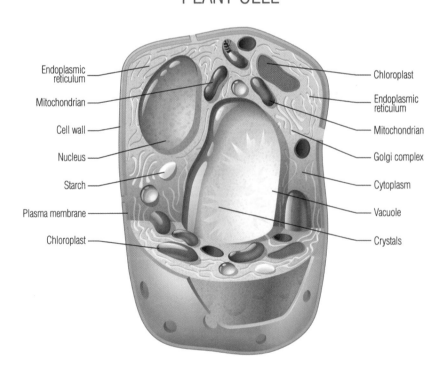

7.

Cell Type	Primary Function
Plant Cell Containing Chloroplasts	carry out the process of photosynthesis
Exterior Root Plant Cells Containing Hairs	absorb water and nutrients from the soil
Phloem Cells Within the Root	conduct glucose from the leaves
Xylem Cells Within the Root	conduct water from roots

8. Sample answer:
Root plant cells gather water and nutrients from the soil. Xylem cells within the root transport the water throughout the plant. Chloroplasts in stem and leaf plant cells use sunlight, carbon dioxide from the air and water from soil to make glucose (food) from the process called photosynthesis. Phloem cells transport glucose from the leaves to other parts of the plant.

9.

List of Ingredients
• sunlight • carbon dioxide (CO_2) • water (H_2O) • chlorophyll
Equipment Needed (Plant Parts)
• roots • stems • leaves • stoma • guard cells • chloroplasts
Step by Step Instructions
1. Roots pull up water from the soil and deliver it through the stems to the leaves. 2. The stoma (with the help of guard cells) breathes in carbon dioxide. 3. The chloroplasts within plant cells absorb energy from sunlight to make chlorophyll. 4. The chloroplasts cook chlorophyll, water, and carbon dioxide to make sugar for plant food and oxygen for animals to breathe.
End Products
sugar and oxygen

Flowering Plants   pp. 142-144

1. Accept any number between 250,000-400,000.

2. Accept any three blue flowering plants: ex. pansies, hydrangeas, irises, etc.

3. Flowering plants reproduce by dropping or spreading.

4.

Pollinated by Insects	Pollinated by Wind
• brightly colored • strong fragrance • large petals (for landing)	• long stamens and pistils • dull colored • unscented • small or no petals

5. Coco de Mer

6. Sample answer*:

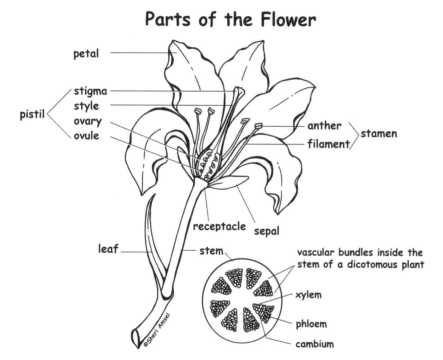

Parts of the Flower

7. Paragraphs will vary but should include things such as: colors of flowers or leaves; fragrance – either nice smelling or horrid stench; food – plants reward pollinators with nourishing nectar or pollen.

8. 125 million years old; Liaoning Province, China

9. Enclosing seeds inside fruit protects the seed until the fruit ripe and ready for germination and drops from the plant.

10. A paleobotanist is a scientist who studies prehistoric plants.

11. hummingbird, butterfly, fly, bumble bee/honey bee, bat, caterpillar

12. fruit

* Parts of the Flower illustration © Sheri Amsel, Exploringnature.org

13.

Making Eggs

The ovary stores ovules which undergo meiosis (cell division) and create a female egg.

Life Cycle
of Flowering Plants

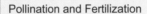

Making Pollen

The anther cells undergo meiosis and become spores which later become sperm (pollen).

Germination and Growth

The embryo's root pushes the seed above ground where it sprouts seed-leaves which drop so it can grow true leaves.

Pollination and Fertilization

Insects transfer pollen from the anther to the stigma. Then the pollen goes down the stigma tube and fuses with the eggs, forming an embryo and endosperm.

Non-Flowering Plants   pp. 145-148

1. A spore is the asexual reproductive body of a fungus or nonflowering plant.

2. Ferns' spores are located on the underside of the fronds.

3. Mushrooms are not plants because they do not produce their own food by photosynthesis; they belong to the fungi kingdom, which gets its food from other organisms.

4. A rhizome is a plant stem that grows horizontally under or along the ground and often sends out roots and shoots. New plants develop from the shoots.

5. A bulb is an underground stem that contains a future plant and stores food for that future plant. A tuber is an enlarged, underground stem that stores food for the currently growing plant.

6.

Non-Flowering Plant	Description
Green Algae	the simplest plant that obtains food through photosynthesis
Mosses	a small, soft-like non-vascular plant that only grows 1-10 cm in height
Ferns	the oldest vascular plant that has stems, leaves and roots; usually grows low to the ground near water
Worts	a plant lacking a woody stem; liverwort; some have medicinal properties; some are pests (weeds)
Horsetails	perennial, rush-like herbs with jointed hollow stems and narrow tooth-like leaves that spread by creeping rhizomes

7. Sample answers for Venn diagram:

Flowering Plants	Both	Non-Flowering Plants
• all vascular • male and female parts • produce seeds • seeds enclosed in fruit • sporophyte phase dominant	• may be vascular • may produce seeds	• some non-vascular • produce spores • seeds not enclosed in fruit • sporophyte and gametophyte phases independent • gametophyte phase dominant in mosses

8. Drawings will vary; sample answers:

Botanical Name: **Marchantia**	Botanical Name: **Drepanocladus**	Botanical Name: **Grimmia**	Botanical Name: **Sphagnum**
Known as: liverwort	Known as: sickle moss	Known as: Antarctica moss	Known as: peat moss
Botanical Name: **Lygodium**	Botanical Name: **Woodsia**	Botanical Name: **Pteridium**	Botanical Name: **Microsorum Pustulatum**
Known as: Old World climbing fern	Known as: cliff fern	Known as: bracken	Known as: kangaroo fern
Botanical Name: **Spruce**	Botanical Name: **Abies**	Botanical Name: **Ginkgo**	Botanical Name: **Sciadopitys**
Known as: Norway spruce	Known as: fir	Known as: maidenhair tree	Known as: umbrella pine

9.

Name of Way to Reproduce	Description
ground layering	Limbs lie on top of ground and take root when dirt and water cover them.
air roots	Branch grows, sends new roots down to the ground, and creates new plant.
runners/side shoots/rhizomes	Runners called rhizomes grow off the underground root system of a plant and then grow upward starting a new plant.
humans cutting or layering the plant	People cut part of plant and then place it in ground or water to root new plant.

10. Paragraphs will vary but should explain asexual reproduction from question 9.

Fruits and Vegetables   pp. 149-152

1. Fruits have seeds; vegetables do not have seeds. Vegetables are parts of the plant itself (i.e. roots, leaves, stem, etc.).

2. Sample answers:

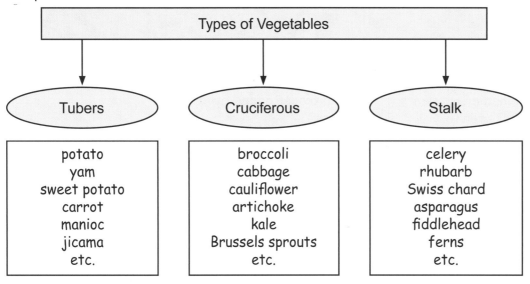

Tubers	Cruciferous	Stalk
potato yam sweet potato carrot manioc jicama etc.	broccoli cabbage cauliflower artichoke kale Brussels sprouts etc.	celery rhubarb Swiss chard asparagus fiddlehead ferns etc.

3. Washington

4. almond

5. about 22 lbs

6.

Fruits	Vegetables
corn	artichoke
rice	bok choy
tomato	celery
wheat	onion

7. The harvest process begins in the fall with flooding the cranberry fields when the berries are ripe and red. Berries are knocked from their vines by machines called beaters. When they float to the surface, they are corralled to one area in the marsh field to load onto trucks.

8. Water is used for growing the vines; irrigation sprinklers water the vines to prevent freezing; and water is used to flood the fields during harvest.

9. Aquaponics is the technique of growing plants without soil in water fertilized by fish.

10. Growing without soil enables vegetables to grow anywhere; recycling water is not wasteful of Earth's most important resource.

11. Sample answer:

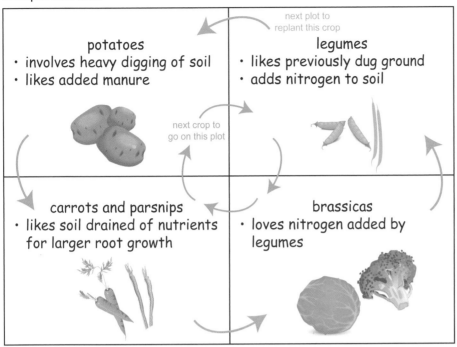

12. Answers will vary. Best result is loam, bright, medium, 8, large.

Trees and Shrubs   pp. 153-156

1. Sample answer:
   Trees <u>improve air quality</u> by cleaning carbon dioxide out of the air and replacing it with oxygen for us to breathe. Trees <u>give shelter</u> to animals: humans use wood to build homes; birds and animals live on and within trees. Trees <u>prevent soil erosion</u> because their massive root systems hold soil in place. Trees <u>provide food</u> in the form of nuts, fruits, and leaves. Trees <u>provide comfort and protection from the sun</u> in the form of shade around parks and buildings.

2. Giant Sequoias

3. Sample answers:

Angiosperms	Gymnosperms
• seeds surrounded by fruit • hardwood • broad leaves • deciduous (change color and die in autumn)	• naked seeds • softwood • needles • evergreen

4.

Angiosperms	Gymnosperms
apple	cedar
magnolia	pine
maple	redwood
oak	spruce

5. Arborists are tree doctors, so someone would hire an arborist if they had a diseased or dying tree to save.

6. Sample answer:

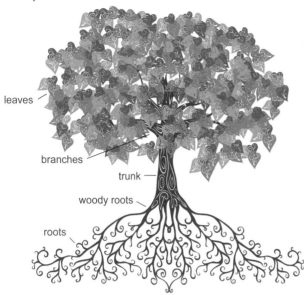

leaves

branches

trunk

woody roots

roots

7. trunks

8. Trees need large woody stems to support their weight and height to reach sunlight above other plants.

9. Dead trees return nutrients to the soil as they decompose.

10.

Clue	Description	Result	
1	cone, needle-like clusters	conifer (evergreen)	
2	needles arranged in clusters	pine	
3	needles are clustered in groups of 5; pine cone scales are thin	Eastern White Pine tree	

11.

Clue	Description	
1	broad, thin, flat leaves	
2	once compound leaves with individual blades (leaflets)	
3	opposite leaf arrangement	
4	pinnately compound leaves with a winged seed that looks like an oar	
		Result
5	7 leaflets with smooth edges	ash tree
6	rounded twigs	
7	leaf scars are nearly straight at the top	green ash tree

Illustrations of Eastern white pine and green ash trees are used with permission of The Arbor Day Foundation.

12. Answers will vary but should include:
    • leaves or needles
    • shape of leaves or groups of needles
    • scales or bark
    • leaf arrangement
    • type of seed or cone
    • branches or twigs

13. Answers will vary. Check math for amount close to $100.

14. Sketches will vary. Check if labels match table in questions 13.

Section 7 – Space

Our Solar System   pp. 158-161

1. Mercury, Venus, Earth, Mars, Jupiter, Saturn, Uranus, Neptune

2. In 2005, scientists defined a planet as:
   a. an object that orbits the sun
   b. spherical in shape
   c. "cleared the neighborhood" in its orbit around the sun – meaning the sun is the main object in the planet's orbital path

3. Pluto is a spherical object that orbits the sun in the Kuiper Belt that contains many more (some larger) objects in the same orbit; therefore, Pluto is a dwarf planet.

4. the sun

5. above 800°F by day; below -300°F by night

6. Venus; size, mass, density

7. water

8. red soil, deep canyons, polar ice

9. a huge, hurricane-like storm

10. Saturn's rings are made up of chunks of ice.

11. rotates on its side

12. Neptune

13. 4½ billion miles or 49 AU from the sun

14. Venus crossing between Earth and the sun; 2117

15. to investigate if Mars ever offered conditions favorable for life

16. slingshot around Earth to propel it toward Jupiter

17. Each moon's gravity pulls the spaceship toward it.

18.

Features	Largest Planet Jupiter	Smallest Planet Mercury
Mass	317 times that of Earth	5% of Earth's
Diameter	88,846 miles or 142,983 km	3,030 miles or 4,876 km
Temperature	-244° F or -153° C	-300° F to 870° F -184° C to 465° C
Distance From the Sun	483 million miles or 777 million km	36 million miles or 57 million km
Length of Day and Year	Day: 9 hours and 55 minutes Year: 4332.59 days	Day: 58.6 Earth days Year: 88 days

19. Letters will vary but should include information from table in question 18.

The Sun   pp. 162-164

1. hydrogen and helium

2.

	helio		centric		Definition
meaning	sun	+	centered	=	the planets revolve around the sun

3. Sample answers: solar power, warmth, light, energy, the sun's gravity keeps us in place in space, weather by heating different parts of Earth at different times

4. Sample answer:

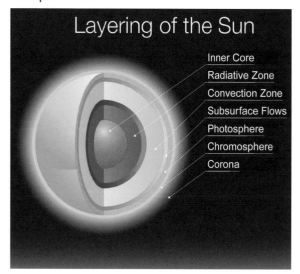

5. ozone layer

6. Fusion is the process of creating energy from combining two atoms of hydrogen to form one atom of helium.

7. The sun's fusion is the main energy source for Earth and fuels the solar system. Life would not exist without the sun.

8. The sun's gravity keeps Earth and the other planets in orbit around the sun.

9.
| The sun's light gives energy to plants. | Plants create food and oxygen through photosynthesis. | Animals eat plants for energy and breathe oxygen. |

10. Drawings will vary but should be colorful.

11. radiation and high energy particles

12. Solar flares, Coronal Mass Ejection (CME)

13. Geomagnetic storms cause auroras and surges in transformers and power lines, corrode electrical currents, and disrupt the ionosphere.

14. Sample answer: Forecasting space weather is needed to protect and prepare our infrastructure from damage to satellites, radars, and communication. Satellites could fail, disrupting our navigational systems in planes and boats, which could cost lives and/or food supply. Telecommunication would be disrupted, affecting people and business.

15.

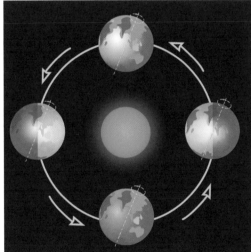

Spring in the Northern Hemisphere; Autumn in the Southern Hemisphere

Summer in the Northern Hemisphere; Winter in the Southern Hemisphere

Winter in the Northern Hemisphere; Summer in the Southern Hemisphere

Autumn in the Northern Hemisphere; Spring in the Southern Hemisphere

The Moon   pp. 165-168

1. A lunar eclipse is the darkening of the moon as Earth passes between the sun and the moon.

2. approximately 2,160 miles (3,475 km)

3. approximately 221,600-252,500 miles (356,700-406,300 km) depending on where it is in the orbit

4. 27 $\frac{1}{3}$ Earth days

5. 27 $\frac{1}{3}$ Earth days

6. rocky material mainly consisting of basalts, anorthosites, and breccia

7. Answers will vary depending on which videos the student chooses.

8. During a preflight test, a fire claimed the lives of three U.S. astronauts.

9. **Moon Landings**

Mission	Date
Apollo 11	July 1969
Apollo 12	November 1969
Apollo 14	January 1971
Apollo 15	July 1971
Apollo 16	April 1972
Apollo 17	December 1972

10. An explosion in one of the oxygen tanks severely damaged the spacecraft, forcing the crew to orbit the moon and return to Earth.

11. The moon has never supported life. Possible reasons: lack of organic compounds, the necessary building blocks for life; lack of water and atmosphere; contamination by meteorites.

12. Scientists continue to study the lunar samples because new advanced technologies are available today that can tell them more information about the moon.

13. The moon appears to shine because it is reflecting the light of the sun.

14. A new moon appears dark because the lighted side is facing away from Earth.

15. We only see one side of the moon because the moon is rotating on its axis while it orbits Earth.

16. A waxing moon is growing larger in lighted area and a waning moon is growing smaller in lighted area.

17.

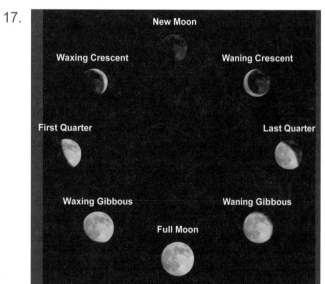

18. Moon poems will vary.

Constellations and Stars   pp. 169-173

1. A constellation is a group of stars to which names and stories were given because they form a pattern resembling an imaginary shape that can be seen in the night sky.

2. Great Bear; Big Dipper

3. A black hole is a place in space where gravity pulls so much that even light cannot get out.

4. Ursa Major, Ursa Mino, Draco, Cassiopeia, and Cepheus

5. Sample answers:

Who	When	Where
Orion, Greek gods and goddesses	Ancient Greece	Greek isles

What
Orion was a great hunter killed out of jealousy or pride and sent to live in the darkest winter sky.

Why
Orion bragged that he could best any animal, so the gods sent a small scorpion to sting him, which killed him. He was placed in the winter sky to be far away from the scorpion, a summer sky constellation.   OR   Orion fell in love with Diana the huntress; her brother was jealous and tricked her into shooting Orion. Out of sadness, she asked that Orion be placed in the darkest winter sky so he could shine brightly.

6. Summaries will vary but must say that Orion was a great hunter; he was killed by either a scorpion or Diana the huntress (by accident) and placed in the winter sky so he could be far from the scorpion or bright for Diana to see him.

7.

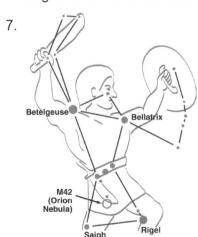

8. Gravitational forces attract dust and gas together to form stars.

9. A star is stable during its main sequence because its forces are balanced- the force of gravity pulling it together is equal to the force of gases expanding or pulling it apart.

Orion illustration used with permission of the University of Texas McDonald Observatory.

10.

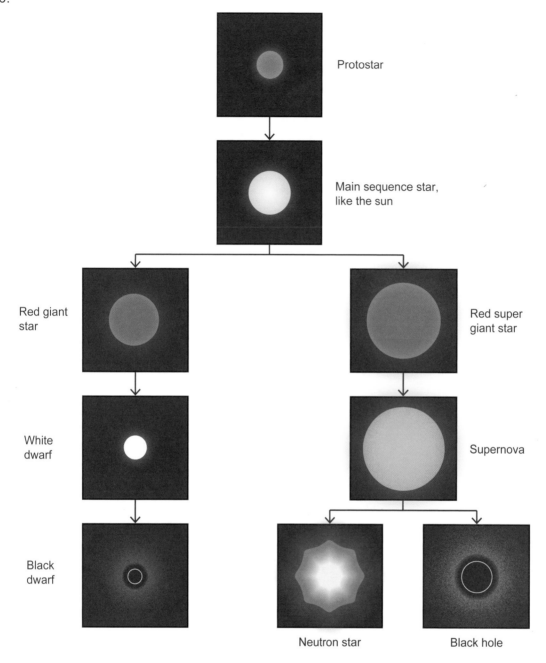

Protostar

Main sequence star, like the sun

Red giant star

Red super giant star

White dwarf

Supernova

Black dwarf

Neutron star

Black hole

11. A small star has a longer life cycle ending as a black dwarf; a large star has a shorter life cycle transforming into a supernova and ending as a neutron star or a black hole.

12. Energy is released when two atomic nuclei join to make a large nucleus.

13. Two hydrogen nuclei join to create one helium nucleus.

14. Our sun is about 5 billion years old; it is in the stable, main sequence stage of its life cycle.

15. A star forming nebula is a swirling mass of dust and gas in outer space that eventually forms stars.

16. A proplet is thought to be young planet in the making and not a star, because it forms alongside a star when spinning dust clumps into a disc.

17. The star affects the nearby discs by heating up the gas within them causing them to shine brightly.

18. Interesting shapes are formed when the stellar wind from the massive star meets the gas in the nebula.

19.

Type	Age	Size	Color
giant	old age; dying	500 times the sun; larger than the orbit of Mars	red

20. blue = hot star; red = cooler star; yellow = just right

21. A star must not be too hot or too cool, and a planet must be the right distance from the star so that liquid water may form.

Space Exploration   pp. 174-177

1. a scientist who studies celestial bodies such as stars, moons, planets, galaxies, nebulae, and other phenomena in the universe

2. the mean distance between Earth and the sun

3. A light year is about 6 trillion miles (9.5 trillion km) or the distance light travels through space in one Earth year.

4. A parsec is a distance equaling about 3¼ light years; a measurement used to measure distances between objects in space.

5.

Astronomers You Should Know

Astronomer	Dates (birth-death)	Country of Birth	Notable Contribution
Nicolaus Copernicus	1473-1543	Poland	Stated Earth and other planets revolved around the sun
Galileo Galilei	1564-1642	Italy	Developed telescope, proved Earth revolved around sun
Sir Isaac Newton	1643-1727	England	Laws of Motion; theories on gravity
Stephen Hawking	1942-	England	Studies black holes and universe's origin
Edmund Halley	1656-1742	England	Predicted orbit of comet; laws of gravity
Edwin Hubble	1889-1953	USA	Hubble's Law: the larger the space object, the faster it is moving away from the Milky Way
Carl Sagan	1934-1996	USA	Brought astronomy to popular culture with his books and TV show, "Cosmos"

6.

Cold War Space Race

Milestone	Date	Country	Astronauts
1st Satellite in Orbit	Oct. 4, 1957	USSR	none
1st Man in Space	April 12, 1961	USSR	Yuri Gagarin
1st American in Orbit	Feb. 20, 1962	USA	John Glenn
1st Woman in Space	June 16, 1963	USSR	Valentina Tereshkova
1st Moon Landing	July 20, 1969	USA	Neil Armstrong, Buzz Aldrin, and Michael Collins
1st Space Lab	May 14, 1973	USA	Conrad, Weitz, Kerwin, Bean, Lousma, Garriott, Carr, Pogue, Gibson
1st Shuttle Mission	April 12, 1981	USA	John Young and Robert Crippen

7. Answers will vary but should be supported by data in question 6.

8. The main purpose of the ISS is to study how humans can live and work in space.

9. Sixteen countries with the U.S. and Russia being the main contributors

10. Sample answer: A maximum of six people can stay on the space station at a time. They can sleep in any orientation, but must be strapped into sleeping bags because of weightlessness. They eat regular food that has been canned or dehydrated for long-term storage. They move inside the ISS by gliding around the compartments and tunnels. They move outside the ISS by wearing a tethered spacesuit. They get oxygen through a process where electricity generated from the sun is used to separate water into hydrogen and oxygen. They work on the ISS conducting experiments, repairing satellites and preparing for new projects.

11. signs of water flow on the surface; signs of ice caps at the north and south poles

12. NASA is exploring Mars with 4 goals: to find out if life ever existed on Mars, to learn about its climate, to learn about its geology, and prepare for humans to go to Mars.

13. Stories will vary.

Asteroids, Meteors, and Comets   pp. 178-182

1. Sample answers:

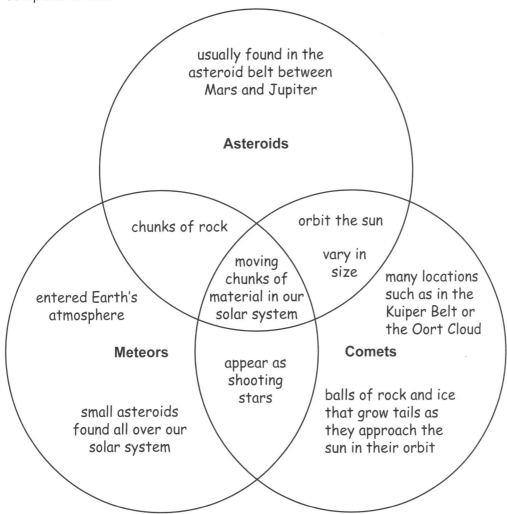

usually found in the asteroid belt between Mars and Jupiter

Asteroids

chunks of rock

orbit the sun

vary in size

moving chunks of material in our solar system

many locations such as in the Kuiper Belt or the Oort Cloud

entered Earth's atmosphere

Meteors

appear as shooting stars

Comets

small asteroids found all over our solar system

balls of rock and ice that grow tails as they approach the sun in their orbit

2.

Name	Width	Location	Contents
Ceres	590 miles (950 km)	asteroid belt between Mars and Jupiter	rock

3. Most meteoroids do not hit Earth's surface because they burn up when they enter Earth's atmosphere and look like shooting stars.

4. A binary asteroid is an asteroid with a moon that orbits the asteroid.

5. Pluto and comets are made of rock and ice; Pluto and some comets orbit the sun in the Kuiper Belt.

6. between Mars and Jupiter

7. The comet broke into many pieces and created explosions similar to a nuclear bomb exploding every second for 13 years and causing a dust cloud on Jupiter bigger than Earth.

8. NASA scientists examined the trajectory of the Russian meteor and plotted its orbit from the asteroid belt. They compared it to the known orbit of DA-14 and concluded that they were not connected at any time because each had its own separate orbit.

9.

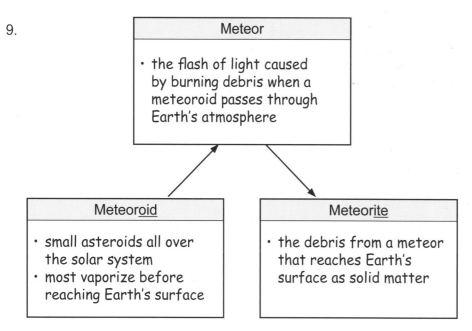

Meteor
- the flash of light caused by burning debris when a meteoroid passes through Earth's atmosphere

Meteoroid
- small asteroids all over the solar system
- most vaporize before reaching Earth's surface

Meteorite
- the debris from a meteor that reaches Earth's surface as solid matter

10. The Oort Cloud is a cloud-like ring in the outer reaches of our solar system, consisting of clumps of icy dust.

11. A comet looks like a dirty snowball about 10 km in diameter.

12. dry ice, ammonia, organic dirt, water

13. The gravitational pull of other stars or large, gaseous objects fling some comets out of the cloud, sending them into a new orbit and bringing them closer to Earth.

14. The discovery of Halley's comet was significant because he used research to predict the comet's orbit and its return every 76 years, enabling scientists to better understand astronomy and the physical universe rather than relying on superstition.

15. Stories will vary, but should include ways to destroy or move an asteroid, meteoroid, or comet off its course.